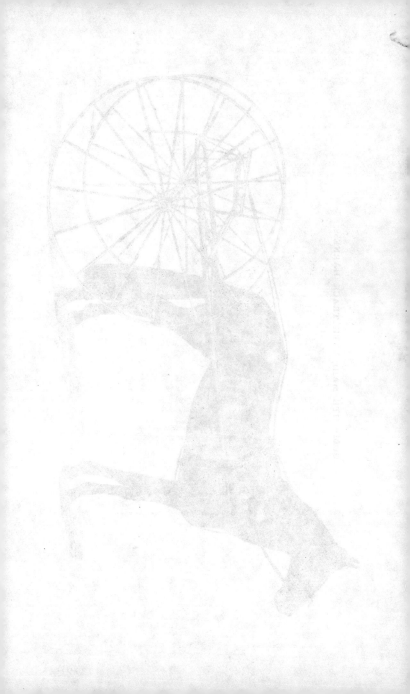

GOLDSMITH MAID, WITH TRACK HARNESS.

THE
HARNESS MAKERS'
ILLUSTRATED
MANUAL.

1977
Reprint Edition

North River Press, Inc.

Library of Congress Cataloging in Publication Data

Fitz-Gerald, William N., 1839-1904.
    The harness makers' illustrated manual.

    Reprint. Originally published: New York:
W.N. Fitz-Gerald. 1875

    1. Harness making and trade. I. Title.
TS1032.F55   1983   685'.1   82-24566
ISBN 0-88427-014-9

Reprinted from the original edition first published in 1875
        by Wm. N. Fitz-Gerald, New York, N.Y.

ISBN: 0-88427-014-9

For additional copies, write to:
        North River Press, Inc.
        Box 241
        Croton-on-Hudson, N.Y. 10520

THE
HARNESS MAKERS'
ILLUSTRATED
MANUAL.

A PRACTICAL GUIDE BOOK FOR MANUFACTURERS AND MAKERS
OF HARNESS, PADS, GIG SADDLES, ETC ,

CONTAINING

DIRECTIONS FOR SELECTING, CUTTING, AND PREPARING
LEATHER; TABLES OF LENGTHS AND WIDTHS FOR
CUTTING TRACK, SINGLE AND DOUBLE ROAD,
COUPE, COACH, EXPRESS, TEAM AND FARM
HARNESS, HALTERS, HORSE BOOTS, ETC.;

RECIPES FOR PREPARING BLACKINGS, STAINS, OILS,
AND LEATHER VARNISHES;

HINTS ON RENOVATING AND REPAIRING HARNESS;

NOTES ON HARNESS MOUNTINGS, WITH DESCRIPTIONS AND
ILLUSTRATIONS OF THE MOST POPULAR
STYLES AND KINDS.

ADAPTED TO THE OFFICE AND THE WORKSHOP.

BY

W. N. FITZ-GERALD,

NEW YORK.

1875.

CONTENTS.

———◆◆———

CHAPTER I.

HARNESS LEATHER.

CHAPTER II.

RUSSET LEATHER.

CHAPTER III.

PATENT LEATHER.

CHAPTER VIII.

DIRECTIONS FOR MAKING UP A BREAST COLLAR SINGLE HARNESS.

CHAPTER IX.

MAKING SINGLE-STRAP TRACK HARNESS.

CHAPTER X.

DIRECTIONS FOR MAKING TEAM HARNESS.

CHAPTER XI.

MAKING GIG SADDLES.

CHAPTER XII.

PADS FOR COACH AND TEAM HARNESS.

CHAPTER XIII.

MAKING HARNESS LOOPS.

CHAPTER XIV.

STITCHING HARNESS.

CHAPTER XV.

MAKING ROUND REINS.

CHAPTER XVI.

COACH AND WAGON BRIDLES.

CHAPTER XVII.

RIDING BRIDLES.

CHAPTER XVIII.

HALTERS.

CHAPTER XIX.

HORSE BOOTS.

CHAPTER XX.

HARNESS MOUNTINGS.

CHAPTER XXI.

BUCKLES.

CHAPTER XXII.

BITS AND BITTING HARNESS.

INDEX OF PLATES.

—————◆—————

NOTICE.

The few advertisements in this book are of established and reliable houses, who manufacture superior goods in their respective lines.

PREFACE.

———••••———

THIS book originated from a desire to furnish harness makers with a condensed practical guide suited to the workshop, office, salesroom, and stable. It treats of leather as furnished to the harness maker by the currier, its texture, strength, adaptability for specific uses ; how to cut, fit, and finish ; measuring for harness ; complete tables for lengths and widths for cutting the various classes in use, whether for the carriage, farm, or road ; bridles, halters, horse-boots, mountings, bits, etc.

The illustrations represent standard styles and kinds of articles used by the trade, and guides for making up.

In the hints on repairing and caring for harness, a large amount of information is furnished the manufacturer and consumer, in a condensed form. The recipes for blacks, stains, varnishes, polishes, etc., have been tested and found reliable ; the whole making a methodical manual indispensable to the progressive harness maker, and useful to every horse owner or other person interested in harness or saddlery. It is the only book of the

kind published in the English language, and supplies a much-needed want. Every care has been
taken to present the subjects treated on in the
plainest manner, and to avoid errors. The
author confidently believes that benefit will result from following the instructions given, and
the standard of harness making be elevated.
Should this anticipation be realized, the time
spent in its preparation will be compensated for.

INTRODUCTION.

THE manufacture of saddlery and harness, exclusive of all collateral branches, stands thirty-fourth in magnitude out of the two hundred and fifty-eight specified industries tabulated in the census report of 1870. At that time there were in the United States 7,607 saddlery and harness establishments, giving employment to 23,557 workmen; all but 841 were males above 16 years of age; employing a capital of $13,935,961; paying in wages $7,046,207; for materials, $16,068,-310; and producing goods to the value of $32,-709,981. Missouri stands first in the list in value of products, but fifth in the number of workmen employed, and second in the wages paid. New-York stands second in value of products, first in every other particular. Pennsylvania, Ohio, Illinois, and New-Jersey are next in order.

By the total figures it will be seen that the average wages of the workmen is about $299 a year, being $78 below the average for the whole country in 1870, and $10 above the average of 1860.

There are but eleven branches of industry in which the number of establishments exceeds those of saddlery and harness, and in view of this fact, the average rate of wages is remarkably good. The harness-maker is called upon to supply harness, saddlery, etc., for 7,145,370 horses, 1,125,415 mules and asses, a total of 8,270,785 animals; yet the total value of products of a year show but $4 a head for each animal—a figure disproportionately small, and one which explains, in part at least, why the trade is less prosperous than it should be. Were it a business which required the investment of a large capital, the case would be different; but as it is, the investment of a few hundred dollars enables a man to engage in a small business which returns him a moderate living, but one that might be lucrative if conducted in a proper manner. The harness maker supplies an article of absolute necessity, and there is no excuse for his placing his prices below fair business rates. If each man in the business would properly estimate the cost of every article, and add thereto a fair percentage of profit, there would be less complaints as to the unprofitableness of the harness trade. In preparing this manual the author has aimed to give information of a practical character to the trade, which will enable those engaged in it to conduct the workshop in a systematic manner. If this end is accomplished, it will be one important step toward making the business a profitable and pleasant one.

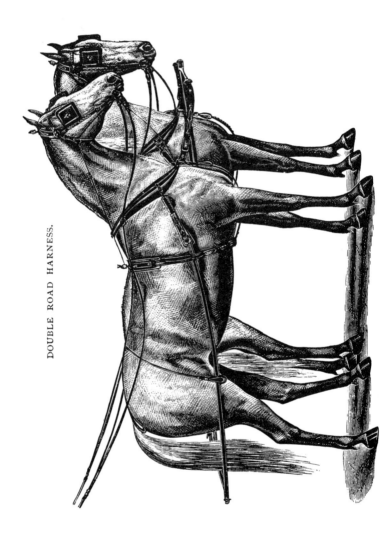

DOUBLE ROAD HARNESS.

THE

HARNESS-MAKERS'

ILLUSTRATED MANUAL.

────◆────

CHAPTER I.

HARNESS LEATHER.

BEFORE entering upon details respecting the practical work of the harness-maker, I shall give some general directions regarding the various kinds of leather used, its adaptation to specific grades and patterns of harness, together with such other details as may serve to assist the manufacturer in selecting his stock.

The familiar adage, "There is nothing like leather," is an old one, and it is true in more senses than one. In the first place, leather is an article of such peculiar structure that those who have spent a lifetime in working it can not give any reliable rules by which an inexperienced person may judge to a certainty of its quality. The grain may be fine, close, and to the eye all that can be desired, the flesh side smooth, of good color, and finely finished, and yet the quality be such as to condemn it as soon as it gets into the hands of the workman. On the other hand, the grain may be coarse and the flesh side badly cleaned, and yet, for actual wear, it may be of good quality. The hides from which it was made may have been taken from old or poorly fed cattle, insufficiently tanned, badly curried with cheap oil and tallow, stuffed to weigh heavy, blacked with strong acids, which have passed through the grain and rendered it hard and brittle, of uneven thickness, the shoulders thin and unfit for general use ; all of which faults are of a serious nature, and yet a long experience, by which the eye and touch are so educated as to detect almost by intuition defects other than the most prominent, is the only safe and reliable guide as to the actual merits of the leather.

There are, however, a few leading tests which assist in the acquiring of the needful experience. The character of the hide before it was tanned may be ascertained, in most cases, by close examination. It is a well-known fact that cattle raised in certain sections of the country produce much finer grained hides, possessing in a greater degree the firm, elastic nature necessary for the production of harness leather, than those raised in other sections. If the hide has been taken from an old and poor animal, the grain will be coarse, uneven, and irregular, the neck hard and rough, the flanks thick and flabby, and the shoulders and hips thin and baggy ; if from a young, well-kept animal, the grain will in most cases be fine, close, and even, the flesh side smooth and of a good color, and the whole side of nearly uniform thickness. Grub-holes are a sure indication of poor hides, but, as they can be so easily detected, it is unnecessary to caution buyers to avoid all having these defects. Short tannage is a very common fault, but it is one that can be detected by cutting a strip from the hide and wetting the freshly-cut edge with the tongue : if the color is uniform throughout, and the cut edge presents a smooth and glassy appearance, instead of being covered with fine fibres, the tannage is good. If, on the other hand, the cut edge presents a fuzzy appearance, feels harsh and rough when dry, and shows a white or light-colored strip through the centre when wet, it is insufficiently tanned, and the wider this light strip the poorer is the tannage.

It frequently happens that leather which has been well tanned is injured in the currying, and it is much more difficult to detect faults arising from this source than those due to short tannages. The grain may have been injured while being tanned, but it is just as liable to injury from the use of strong acid blacks, which, while giving it a deep black color, cause it to become hard and brittle. The best and most reliable test for detecting this fault is to bend a narrow strip, flesh sides together, and close it down between the teeth ; if the grain is hard and brittle, it will surely break off short, so as to show the natural color of the leather underneath. If, however, the leather is extra heavy, this test will be likely to rupture the grain, whether the quality be good or bad ; but if good, it will have the appearance of having been torn asunder instead of broken off short. If the hard grain has been produced by strong acids, which have burned it, a freshly-cut edge will show to what depth they have penetrated, and there will be black streaks well down into the fibres below the grain. The use of impure oils or grease is also a source of much annoyance, it being very difficult, in fact almost impossible, to detect the fault until after the harness has been made up and exposed for a time in the show-case, when the tell-tale gum-spots will appear on the surface, exposing the fraud, though not until the manufacturer has suffered much loss by the depreciation in the value of his harness. It sometimes happens that these gum-spots will appear upon the grain before the side has been cut. When this is the case the leather may be treated as we have directed in Chapter V., and future gumming will be prevented.

These points seem to assist in the detection of the above-mentioned faults, but they can not be relied upon under all circumstances ; frequent handling and close observation will alone give the eye and touch the training necessary for the intelligent selection of the different qualities. Good leather, in the language of one of the best known and most experienced men in the harness-leather trade, should be " solid, but not hard ; mellow, but not soft "—qualities that can not be explained, but which can be detected instantly by one who has the requisite experience. In this country there are three kinds of leather employed by harness-makers—namely, oak, hemlock, and union (oak and hemlock) tanned, all of which are used to a considerable extent. All other conditions being equal, however, oak-tanned leather is by far the best. It is firmer, but not so hard as hemlock, the fibre is finer and more dense, and, as a natural result, is not so easily affected by water; it also works up finer, takes a much better finish, is more easily worked, and possesses more of the qualities indispensable to the production of good harness—strength and pliability—than any other tannage. Hemlock leather is harder; of a dark red color, which greatly interferes with its taking a good black, and also causes the latter to assume a dingy brown appearance on exposure to the elements ; the grain is more open and appears coarser ; it wets up quickly, and does not dry out as soft as does oak leather ; it is harder to stitch, and is inferior in strength, particularly when the strap is placed in a position where the strain comes on a short bend or on the edge. It is also much heavier. A side of hemlock will weigh from eight to ten per cent more than a side of oak leather of equal spread and thickness, a difference that makes up for the margin in price between the two kinds. " Union" leather is either tanned with mixed oak and hemlock liquors, or first tanned with hemlock, and afterwards retanned with oak, the latter operation giving it a much lighter color than it originally possessed ; in some cases the color on the flesh side being so light as to deceive the buyer who is unacquainted with this kind of leather. The grain is close and, as a rule, finer than either oak or hemlock, but for harness this leather is inferior to oak in every respect, and but a little better than hemlock. It weighs nearly as heavy as the latter, and possesses no qualities that recommend it to the buyer who desires good stock.

In some sections of the country, hemlock leather is made with much care, the hides being closely selected, well tanned, and curried with the best oil and grease. Prepared in this manner, it gives satisfaction when not brought into direct competition with oak-tanned stock; but, no matter how much care may have been exercised, it is inferior to oak-tanned leather with which the same pains have been taken, and there is but one condition under which it should receive the preference, and that is when the choice lies between inferior oak and superior hemlock.

The following general advice may be of value to harness-makers and manufacturers of harness leather. Select hides of young steers or heifers which were in the best condition when killed : they only possess the requisites of fineness of grain,

uniformity of thickness, and strength of fibre.
A cow or bullock hide is entirely unfitted for
this kind of leather; the butt of the former is liable to be thick and the shoulder thin, while the
latter will be thick at the head and belly, thin
and soft at the butt.   Having found such a hide,
examine it further and see that it has not been
damaged by scratches.   These, though apparently simple, are very injurious, as they can not be
entirely removed, and will show upon the grain
as soon as the leather is dampened by the workmen.   See that there are no warble or grub holes
along the back.   These are not likely to be found
in hides taken from cattle that are killed in the
summer or fall.   Next ascertain whether the hide
has been damaged by the butcher or not.   If it
has been cut, it should never be used for harness
leather.   Length is an important consideration,
and many hides are seriously damaged in this
respect by the butcher having cut the animal's
throat from ear to ear, thus shortening the hide
by severing the cheeks from the body.

  Tanning, though not a portion of the harness-
maker's business, should be understood by him
so far as to enable him to distinguish between the
various products.   Oak-tanned is superior to any
other now in use because of its being tougher
and more pliable; but even oak-tanned may not
be good.   There are two general methods of
tanning: one the sole leather, by which the leather is made firm and hard; the other the upper
leather, by which the leather is made pliable and

tough. By the first method greater weight is
secured, but the quality is unsuited to the use of
the harness-maker. Some tanners follow the
former method in part, and thereby secure a
greater weight, but they can not produce a good
quality. This leather can be detected while
working it by its hard, sole-leather-like character.
It does not work well in rounds, or when being
raised, and is more likely to break when subjected
to a sudden strain.

In addition to these features of tanning,
there is what is known as the short-tanned,
this leather coiling like a piece of tin, and when
cut it shows a pale streak through the centre. Then there is the limy leather, with a loose,
wrinkled grain, or puffed up beyond its proper
thickness, which will, upon being worked, stretch
and fall away to its natural substance. There is
also the black-oak tannage. This leather shows
a greenish-yellow appearance in spots upon
the flesh side. It is soft, and possesses less
strength than white-oak leather. Well-tanned
leather is too often injured in being curried; the
use of poor oils and grease causes the " gum,"
" spew," or " fry," as it is known in different localities ; if properly curried with good oils, this
pest of the harness-maker will not appear. Leather that has been well curried will possess a surface free from roughness or wrinkles, and will be
smooth and silky to the touch.

The buyer, therefore, should insist upon the seller furnishing him with hides such as have been

recommended, reasonably free from scratches, warble or grub holes, or cuts by the butcher, of fine, mellow tannage, and curried in the best manner with pure oil and grease. Perfection is not to be expected; the harness-maker should aim to secure leather possessing the minimum of defects. Hard leather is sometimes made to feel mellow and to appear tough by being moistened by the currier. The dampness may be detected by placing the palm of the hand upon the thickest part of the side. Such leather shrinks in weight, and proves a poor purchase to the buyer.

Next in importance to the procuring of a good quality of leather is the selection of that which possesses the requisite weight and strength for the kinds of harness designed to be made, and the particular parts for which it is intended.

So well is this understood by leading harness-manufacturers who make up full lines, that they never cut a harness from a single side, but select the leather carefully and use a specific grade or weight for each particular strap; while the leading custom manufacturers purchase or cut only backs of the best quality. The great majority, however, buy their leather in small quantities, and by so doing commit the error of not procuring a proper assortment. As a rule, they select the weight best adapted to the greater portion of their work, and when lighter stock is needed they resort to the splitting-machine, entailing on themselves extra labor, and wasting no inconsiderable amount of leather, besides materially weakening the straps thus manipulated, as the portion of the flesh side which is removed is the strongest part of the stock.

If extra heavy straps are needed, three thicknesses of leather are used, which in most cases calls for the use of the splitting-machine to prevent overweight, whereby further loss is incurred. If, instead of following this course, they would assort the sides so as to provide themselves with a full line of weights, from six to twenty pounds a side, they would at all times possess leather adapted to every requirement except the heaviest truck-harness, which calls for the heavier grades. Light weights are needed for bridles, no matter what kind of harness is to be made, and, as a rule, sides weighing fourteen pounds and under can be cut to good advantage for this purpose. Traces, back-bands, and breeching-straps require heavier leather, and hides suitable for these particular straps should always be kept on hand. A few years' experience will enable any man to determine the proper weights and proportions for his line of business, and he can procure assorted stock just as easily as he can any single weight.

Light road-harness of the best quality, whether single or double, is made up of two thicknesses and stitched throughout. The leather used should be of the finest quality of light weights, ranging from fourteen to sixteen pounds to the side for the harness proper, and eight to twelve pounds for the bridles, these weights being better adapted to this class of harness than the heavier grades that need to be split in order to reduce them to the required thickness. The grain is generally fine and the fibre strong; it fits up well, retains its shape, and finishes smooth and soft.

The track-harness, which is now one of the most popular styles in use for trotting-horses, is made up of single straps throughout, excepting the back-bands. The leather best adapted to this style is that made from fine-grained, young hides, the weight being about sixteen pounds to the side for all but the bodies; these, being also single, should be of a lighter weight, or they will have to be skived off on the under side to prevent the edges curling up. For bridles, the same weight should be used as for light road-harness.

The medium grade of light single harness is generally made up with single straps and lined points. For this style a heavier leather is required, except for the bridle, in order to obtain the requisite firmness and strength, the best weight being from sixteen to eighteen pounds to the side. These weights also answer well for all grades of single or double harness up to those requiring one and one quarter inch traces, though it is better to use heavier weights for traces, hold-backs, and back-bands.

For light coach-harness, the best weight is about eighteen pounds to a side; but if extra heavy traces are used, it is better to select leather sufficiently heavy to allow of the employment of only two thicknesses, thus obviating the necessity of a filling-in piece. If the latter is used, it should be of quite light leather.

Coach and coupé harness require heavy weights, particularly for traces, hold-backs, back-bands, and breeching-straps ; for all other straps, except-ing bridles, eighteen to twenty pounds to a side are good weights, but the latter should be made from sides weighing about fourteen pounds.

Light express-harness, being made up of single straps, requires the use of sides weighing from eighteen to twenty pounds each ; the bridles, however, should be made from stock of about the same weights as that used for coach-harness. These weights also answer well for farm and the lighter grades of team harness, while heavy truck and cart harness requires the use of the heaviest grades of leather in the market. The above weights are those of the average spread of oak-tanned sides ; extra large or small hides, or those tanned with hemlock, may be gauged by these.

Grain leather is much used for folds, and, as a rule, the bellies, or at least the lower portions of trimmed hides, answer well for this pur-pose ; though the finest, for coach and light har-ness, is made from sides weighing sixteen pounds or under, while for team and truck harness a heavier grade is required.

CHAPTER II.

I N selecting rein leather, the same tests as to quality should be employed as with harness leather, as it is in every respect the same with the exception that, instead of being colored black, it is bleached, and afterwards stained brown or some other color. The latest freak of fashion is to bleach it quite light and then color it with a yellowish-brown stain, so as to produce what is known as cuir-color, a very light, almost imperceptible brown; in fact, the shade is nearer to the natural color of fine oak-tanned leather than any thing else, and the stain used is more for the purpose of producing a uniform shade than establishing a new color. When this color is employed, very little stain is needed on the edges of straps to bring them up to the same shade as the grain; and where it can be done, the harness-maker will find it to his advantage to procure of the leather-manufacturer the same kind of stain as is used to color the grain, the beauty of a russet rein depending quite as much upon its uniformity of color as upon its make. The brown and yellow stains can be made very easily, but those used to produce the soft, fine shades are part of the lea-

ther-manufacturer's stock-in-trade, and their preparation is kept a secret, at least until fashion has
adopted some new color as the favorite.

In selecting rein leather, it is bad policy to
choose any thing but the best quality. Poor leather
works harder, does not keep its shape as well, and
takes a less uniform shade when stained, particularly when it is short-tanned, as the untanned
centre presents a darker shade than the portion
that is well filled with bark. Then, too, if the
grain is hard it is liable to crack while being
made up, or upon being bent while in use. A
pair of russet reins will contain about one pound
of leather, and the trifling difference in the cost
between the highest and lowest priced stock
should not be sufficient inducement to the harness-
maker to jeopardize the lives of his customers by
the use of inferior, unsafe reins.

Hand-part leather, like that for the reins, should
be of the very best quality, and all the tests that
are applied to other kinds are equally effectual
for this, while it should also be soft and pliant. It
is customary among harness-makers who use but
a small amount of rein-leather to cut their folds
for hand parts from the same side as they do the
rounds.

This is a mistake, entailing additional cost without the gain of a single advantage. Rein leather
in most cases is too heavy for folds, and must be
split to reduce it to the proper thickness. This
process removes some of the strongest portion of
the leather, besides occupying the time of the

workman. A cheaper and much better plan is to
procure hand-part leather that has been made expressly for the purpose. It is of lighter weight,
much stronger in prcportion to its thickness,
and, when cut to the proper width, is ready
for the workman to make up. For flat hand
parts the leather should be equally as heavy
as that used for the rounds; it can be cut from
the same sides as the rounds if desired, but, as
it is generally too hard, the workman is compelled
to resort to some method of softening it, such
as pulling it around a post, rolling and working, etc. For flat hand parts, grained leather is
quite popular, and looks well.

When the harness-maker can not readily procure this, he can obtain very nice grained hand
parts by boarding or breaking the grain in the
same manner as is done by the curriers, as follows : cut a piece of leather from the side, of the
full width needed for two pairs of hand parts, as
a piece of the requisite width for one pair would
be too narrow to work well; lay the strip on a
table, the grain side up, and with a board, such as
is used by curriers, crease the grain, commencing
at the front corner on one end, and giving the
leather a half roll diagonally across the strip, con-
tinuing to work it at the same angle until the
other end is reached; then commence at the front
corner of the other end, and board it at the same
angle as the first, until the end is reached where
the work was begun. By this means, the creases
in the grain will cross each other and form the dis-

tinctive feature from which the leather gets its name. The fineness of the graining depends upon the amount of labor applied. In a little time the workman will acquire all the experience necessary for the production of a fine, even grain.

To the harness-maker using but little of this kind of hand-part leather, graining in this manner is a matter of economy. The labor needed to produce the desired surface does even more than this, as it breaks down and softens the leather, making it as pliant as can be desired.

Buff leather is also much used for hand parts. It is made of the same quality of stock as the other kinds, but is not stained, the grain being buffed by the currier to remove the gloss and give it a white, furried appearance. It is a soft, pliant leather, and is one of the best kinds in use for hand parts, as, in addition to its softness and good appearance, it will not soil the most delicate fabrics.

Another light-colored leather, and one a good quality of which it is difficult to procure, is that known as loop leather. This, unlike the kinds before mentioned, is not curried with oil, or at least the quantity of grease of any kind employed is very small. It must be solid, and yet possess a mellow grain that will readily take a crease and retain it. If in creasing up the work, one mark when placed in close proximity to another obliterates it, or decreases its depth in the least, a good piece of work can not be made, and only by the exercise of the greatest care can even an ordinary job be produced. If, however, the grain is mellow, each impression made by the creaser becomes permanently set, and the adjoining one, no matter how near it may be, is equally well defined. For this reason, in selecting a side, make good tannage, mellow grain, and a solid body the tests.

The lack of uniformity in thickness is a matter of no importance ; indeed, instead of being a detriment, as is the case with all other leather used by harness-makers, it is a positive advantage, as the shoulders and other thin parts can be used for check and other light loops, while the thick butts are of the proper weight for trace and similar heavy loops, all the intermediate thicknesses being available for the various loops for other parts.

BUYING LEATHER.

In purchasing leather, the buyer is compelled to depend much upon the honor of the seller in other respects than the determination of the quality, excepting in the case of weight stock, which is sold by the pound, the weight being ascertained at the time of sale. With trimmed stock, however, the case is different in most markets. This leather is marked with its weight while in the rough, and after it is trimmed and curried there are no means of ascertaining the correctness of the brand. It is claimed that a side of leather weighing eighteen pounds in the rough will lose about four pounds in the currying and trimming. No reliance however, can be placed upon this estimate ; for if the flesh side is not well cleaned, and the currier is desirous of misleading, the leather may be stuffed with cheap oil until the finished is equal to the rough weight.

Backs as well as trimmed sides are sold by the rough weight, with an additional charge of $1 and $1.50 each for dressing. Recently, however, a leading New-York manufacturer has adopted the plan of selling backs by their actual weight at the time of sale, the price charged being 82 cents per pound, which is, as near as can be ascertained, the actual cost of that bought by the pound, and to which an extra charge has been added for finishing. The latter is the most simple method, and will no doubt come into general use when the advantages are fully understood.

The buyer, however, is at liberty to take or leave the bellies—in the latter case the value by weight being deducted from the bill. These weigh, as a rule, four pounds. Thus a side of leather which weighed eighteen pounds in the rough, if properly fleshed and curried will lose four pounds by this process and three or four pounds more by cropping, leaving about eleven pounds of prime leather in the back, for which the buyer pays as though in the rough stock—eighteen pounds, less the three or four pounds deducted if the bellies are not wanted. Therefore, in buying a back, 48 cents a pound would be charged for eighteen pounds of leather, and $1.50 added for dressing, making the total cost $8.70, after deducting for the bellies, leaving eleven pounds of prime leather, to be paid for at a cost of about 80 cents a pound, or nearly double the apparent quotation.

In trimmed stock, the difference between the actual and the quoted price is much less, but the buyer pays for the bellies as well as the backs. The price charged per pound is, however, about 2 cents less for the same quality, in which case an eighteen-pound side would cost $8.28, and the actual weight would be about fourteen pounds, making the leather cost about 59 cents a pound, a difference of about 21 cents a pound between it and the backs. It will be seen by this that any false branding of the rough weight causes a marked advance in the price, and should teach the importance of buying trimmed stock of honest, reliable men, and of avoiding speculators, who offer extra inducements in the way of low prices, as the latter are sure to be made up by increased weight.

CHAPTER III.

PATENT LEATHER.

G LAZED, or, as it is more frequently called, patent leather is now extensively used in the manufacture of harness, pads, gig-saddles, and winkers, they being seldom made of other kinds, while for ornaments such as tabs, tug-ends, fronts, etc., it is deemed almost indispensable; like plain leather, it is made both of good and poor material, and finished to correspond.

The finest quality is made of well-assorted hides, tanned with young oak bark, weak liquors being used at first, and gradually strengthened each day until the proper degree is reached, ample time being given to thoroughly tan the leather before it is removed from the vats. All hides that are to be used for thin leather are then split.

The first split taken from the flesh side is small, and is known as the "junior," and is seldom finished in glazed stock; following this is one or more full splits according to the thickness of the hide. The splits are always finished smooth, the grain being largely used for enamel leather, though it is also finished as grain, collar, binding, etc.

Running the hide through the splitting-machine has long been acknowledged to be detrimental to the leather, owing to the severe strain to which it is subjected, but the introduction of the belt-knife machine for splitting removes much of this objection, as the hide is split without being strained in the least. The processes of varnishing, drying, and finishing, while determining the quality of the leather, are foreign to the business of the harness-maker; but there are points which he should understand in order to be able to judge of the quality of the leather. The first of these is the condition of the finished surface, which should be smooth, the coat of color and varnish being of sufficient thickness to give a pure color, while on skirting, winker, and other heavy stock the varnish should be thicker than on light leathers, as these are seldom bent while being worked. Light leather, such as collar and binding, is always worked over round frames, and if the glazed coat is too heavy it is liable to crack, thus defacing the surface. This is particularly the case with collar-leathers, which in too many cases are but the thinnest splits, selected without regard to their adaptability to the required purpose, whereas they should be of extra soft stock, coated as thinly as possible with the best grade of varnish. The severe treatment it receives while being shaped to the collar is sure to impair the surface even of the best. The grades of leather known as grain winker, skirting, collar, etc., command a much higher price

than that known as splits. With the thinner qualities there is some advantage in using the grain,
as the surface preserves its original appearance
much better after being worked than does split
stock; for winker and skirting, however, the
grain does not possess any special merit, except
what it may gain from not being put through the
splitting-machine, as thin hides are selected, and
they are reduced to a uniform thickness by the
knife. The varnish is applied to the flesh sides, and
is therefore open to the same objections as to split
stock. The prejudice against the latter is a sense-
less one, and harness-makers pay dearly for yielding to it and selecting grain stock at higher rates.

Enamel leather is always made of the grain
side, and its quality must be determined by its
softness to the touch, purity of color, and fineness
of finish. The prices of patent leather vary to an
extent that creates surprise in the minds of
buyers who are unacquainted with the causes.

These exist from the very commencement. In
the first place, the hides themselves may be of an
inferior quality. When they are limed and prepared for the tanner, they may be placed in
strong hemlock liquors and partially tanned,
after which they are split and then retanned in
oak liquor for the purpose of producing a light
color. They are also submitted to various manipulations, unknown to any but the initiated, for
the purpose of giving a good appearance to the
leather without increasing the expense, which in
no way improves the quality. After being other-

wise prepared for the varnish, the hides are placed upon a frame, and by means of powerful jack-screws stretched to their utmost extent, whereby an increased measurement of from five to seven feet is given to each. They are then glazed and finished to look as well as prime stock, and can be sold at a marked reduction in price compared with the former; but the buyer who imagines he has saved two cents a foot by purchasing these hides pays for five or seven feet of leather, the greater part of which is sure to be lost, in a few months, by shrinkage. The worst feature of this excessive stretching is that the leather, being extended to its utmost capacity while wet, can not be worked smooth when used over irregular shapes, as all the stretch is taken out of it while being manufactured. This cheap stock therefore costs nearly as much as the best qualities, is more difficult to work, and is less durable when put to actual use. The care of patent leather in stock in order to prevent loss is a matter of considerable importance. When practicable, all thick stock should be hung up in a cool, dry room, while thin stock, both enamelled and smooth, should be rolled, thin paper being placed next to the glazed surface.

There is another matter that is well worthy the attention of buyers—namely, the season in the year when the leather is made, this having much to do with its durability.

The best leather is produced in cool weather, the poorest during the hot months of July and

August. The latter is somewhat less liable to become sticky when exposed to the sun, but it is almost sure to crack during cold weather, sometimes when not in use, and there are very few leather-manufacturers who are willing to warrant stock not made in cold weather. Harness-manufacturers should therefore look well to this matter, as cracked patent leather destroys the appearance of their work.

CHAPTER IV.

CUTTING HARNESS.

THE cutting of harness leather so as to avoid waste, and to secure that best suited to the requirements of each individual strap is a subject of the first importance to every harness-maker, no matter what the extent of his business may be. Leather scraps are of no value, though every piece has been paid for, while the use of the softest and weakest part of the leather in straps that receive the greatest amount of strain insures the production of an inferior harness, be it ever so well made up. The cutter therefore lays the foundation for, and upon his skill depends much of, the manufacturer's success. In large factories this is well understood, and the most skilful men are employed at high wages to cut up stock.

These cutters are of necessity governed by the grade of harness and kind of stock used, and are guided solely by their own judgment, there being no general rule that can be applied to each individual case. The small manufacturer, however, is differently situated, and by following rules that have been adopted by those who have had years of experience in the best shops of the country, he will not only save stock, but produce much more durable harness. The cutter receives his leather in three forms, known to the trade as weight stock, trimmed stock, and backs; these are illustrated by Fig. I. The extreme outline shows the side in full; this is sold as weight stock—that is, by its actual weight at the time of purchase. The dotted line commencing at the root of the tail and passing down the back end, along the belly and up the front to the top, shows the general form of the hide after being trimmed, though in some cases the trimming consists of merely cutting off a few of the most prominent points and slightly straightening the edges. The dotted line A, running parallel with the length of the hide, indicates the bottom line of what is known as the back (the width of which is governed by the condition of the hide itself), the line of separation being drawn just above the thin portion of the flank, the position of which is shown by the dotted line B, the ends being trimmed the same as in trimmed stock.

A harness-maker who does a small business of a general nature will find it most profitable to buy weight stock of the best quality ; he can then crop it, as it is called—that is, cut the side in two parts at or about the line A. This will give him three straight edges to work from in cutting out straps for repairing and other small jobs, obviating the necessity of splitting his leather to obtain straps for the requisite thickness, and also avoiding the spoiling of a trace or rein by cutting a

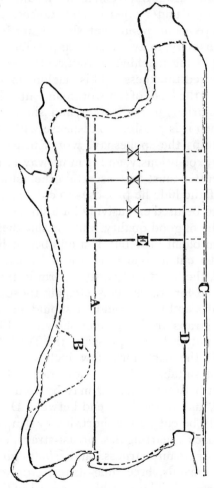

FIG. 1.

small strap from the back, as he would be compelled to do under other circumstances. In cutting, there is one point that should not be over-
looked, namely, to avoid as far as possible the use
of the splitting-machine to reduce the straps to
the required thickness. This machine materially
facilitates the labor of the workman, but it is posi-
tively injurious to the leather, and should not be
used when it is possible to dispense with it. For
small straps the spokeshave works nearly if not
quite as expeditiously, and is in no way injurious.

The cutter must first ascertain the actual condition of the hide he proposes to cut up. If one
hide is to be used exclusively for a single harness,
it must be of good quality, uniform thickness, and
free from blemishes; but if a number of harness
are to be cut at one time, the sides should be
selected, the finest and most uniform in thickness
being used for traces, reins, etc., but those having
thick butts and thin shoulders should be cut up
in short straps, in the manner shown by Fig. 1.

The dotted line represents the straightened
edge. If the back for a few inches below this
line is of suitable thickness for traces, that portion of it between C and D may be used for this
purpose, and all the back end between D and A,
back of E, be cut up for short, heavy straps, such
as hold-backs, martingales, breast-straps, etc., for
express or team harness, and shaft girth-bil-
lets, back-bands, breeching-straps, etc., for car-
riage-harness. The shoulder forward of the line
E, being thin, is admirably adapted to docks, and

should be cut as shown by lines X. Being cut across the grain, they work up smoothly on the inside, the few wrinkles that are formed by bending being easily rubbed out. The remaining portion of the side, such as bellies, etc., be cut into folds and linings, and the short, firm pieces into buckle-chapes and short billets, thus utilizing every part.

To cut a single harness out of a side of leather requires an entirely different process, which will be explained in detail, the side with the different sections being shown by Fig. 2.

A side for this purpose if of closely trimmed stock should weigh about sixteen pounds, the rough brand being seventeen or eighteen.

The back should first be straightened as shown by the dotted line A, which should be drawn as nearly as possible on a line parallel with the centre of the back-bone. It may be necessary to waste a little stock to do this, but the advantage of having the fibre of the side parallel with the edges of the straps will more than repay the loss occasioned. Having straightened the centre cut of the tail as shown by line 1, then measure off from line 1 the full length required for the traces and reins, cut in line 2 of the same depth as line 1, and cut the requisite straps for these parts. This will leave the back perfectly straight, unless, as sometimes occurs, the side from the root of the tail is shaped like that shown. In this case, straighten the new line by cutting off the small piece back of line 1, and cut the straight cross-line 3, then measure from the back end the length required for the breeching-straps, and cut these from B. This will leave the edge with a jag at line 4, which should be straightened before cutting any other straps from the back end.

It may be well to state at this point that keeping a straight edge the full length of the side, and cutting the cross-lines no deeper than absolutely necessary to release the straps, are two important considerations, which if not observed will result in no little waste of leather. A very common fault of the cutters, and one that should be carefully guarded against, is the holding of the knife at an acute angle, and cutting from the under side, allowing it to cut into the side of leather in order to release the end of the strap previously slit off.

The offset C, forward of the cross-line 4, can be cut up into layers for girths. These being removed, the edge is once more straight, and the cutter should measure off from the back end section the requisite length for the turn-back or hip-straps, cutting in on line 5, the same lengths answering for shaft tug-billets and back-bands, giving a pair of each by cutting in the middle. Sections H and M may be cut up into breast collar-layers, crown-pieces, breeching-layers, neck-straps, nose-pieces, martingale-layers, etc., and, if not too heavy, into check-pieces, throat-latches, and centre check-pieces in the order named. Section E should be cut into straps that require rounding, such as checks, round throat-latches, etc., and section K into linings and points,

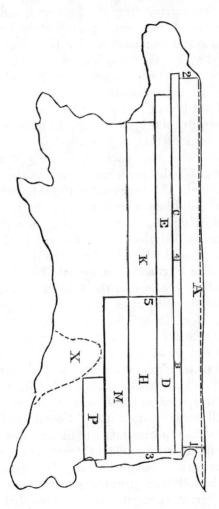

FIG. 2.

always measuring from the back end, and retaining the head and neck part that is left in as large a piece as possible. By this time all the heaviest straps are provided for and the best portion cut up. The section X, indicated by the dotted line, represents the thin, baggy flank, which should not be cut up into straps, but can be used to good advantage for linings to winkers. Section P, back of this, is just what is required for winker-braces, the back end being thick, the leather gradually growing thinner as the flank is approached. All that part of the side forward of the flank, and below section K, can be worked up into folds, cutting the breeching, breast-collar, neck-straps, belly-bands, and crowns in the order named. The thick end back of the flank, and below section P, can be cut up into buckle-chapes, short billets, etc., while the thin ends and other irregular-shaped pieces can be used to good advantage for linings for tabs, etc. It is not claimed that this system of cutting can be strictly carried out in all cases, but by following the general order given, the cutter will be sure of securing just such leather as is needed for the particular straps named, and will at the same time avoid all unnecessary waste. Certain defects in the side may necessitate slight changes in the section indicated for certain straps, but when the blemishes are removed the regular order given should be followed, providing that the straps requiring great strength are not crowded below the line A in Fig. 1.

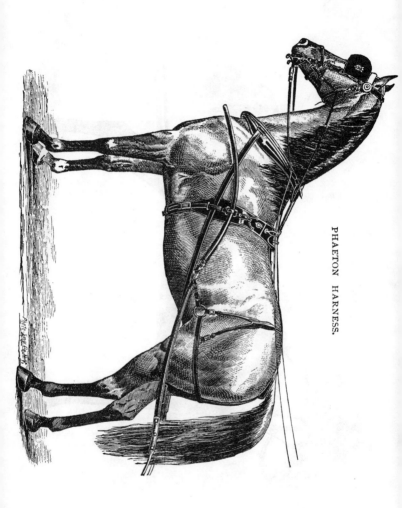

PHAETON HARNESS.

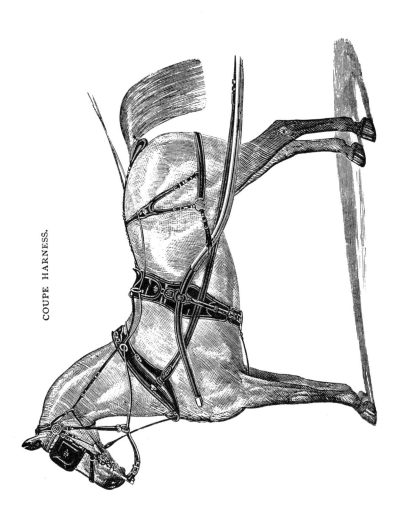

COUPE HARNESS.

CHAPTER V.

IN the manufacture of fine harness, where the straps are to be worked up full and to artistic patterns, the best quality of oak leather should be used, as, it being well curried, the manner of working it is less complicated than when commoner grades are employed. The reason for this is, that only the firm portion of the leather is used, the bellies, flanks, etc., being cut all off, leaving a narrow strip called the back, from eighteen to twenty-two inches wide. This leather requires to be moistened with a sponge and water, but there are few harness-makers who wet it to any considerable extent. The practice, however, of one of the leading manufacturers of this country is to place all the straps in a vat of water, allowing them to remain immersed until the grain shows signs of the tallow coming to the surface. They are then removed, wiped, and hung up until the surface moisture is dried off, when they are handed over to the fitter, who rolls the whole in a coarse cloth, afterwards taking them out one at a time, and fitting them up. It is claimed that this treatment prepares the leather for working up much better than when it is merely damp-

cned, and that the little oil and grease forced out
can easily be replaced without any detriment to
the leather.

Curriers, however, condemn this treatment
of fine, well-finished stock, but experience has
shown that leather thus manipulated can be worked up into the finest harness, the finish on the
grain being soft and clear and the edges smooth,
the leather retaining its softness as long as that
which has only been moistened. While there is a
marked reduction in the labor necessary in fitting
it up, it is evident that there is something gained
by pursuing this method.

There is in the market large quantities of well-
tanned but poorly-curried stock. This is far
preferable to poorly-tanned leather, no matter
how well it may be curried, if properly treated
by the harness-maker. The right course to pur-
sue with this quality is to soak the leather until
it is well moistened to the centre, the length of
time necessary varying so greatly with different
kinds that it is impossible to give any other
guides than the appearance of the grease on the
surface. The "testing-strap" is also sometimes
employed. A small scrap of the leather, being
soaked, is placed in the water with the straps,
and when the workman thinks the leather is sufficiently wet, he cuts this strap and ascertains
whether or not the moisture has penetrated to
the centre. When sufficiently wet, the straps are
removed from the vat and hung up until the surface moisture has dried off. Each strap is then

taken in hand, and if the leather' has been badly fleshed, a spokeshave is used to remove all the superfluous stock. This is done by laying the strap on the bench, grain side down, securing the end with an awl, and with a sharp tool cutting off the loose scraps and thin, veiny portions. Care should be taken, however, to avoid cutting away any more of the flesh side than is absolutely necessary, as the leather is weakened by so doing. After being cleaned off, the leather should be rubbed on the flesh side with a slicker, and laid out on a board grain side down ; then with brush give each strap a coat of melted tallow, warm enough to run freely, but not sufficiently hot to injure the leather, and brush it well to work in all the grease possible. Allow the straps to remain coated with tallow for twelve hours at least, by which time the moisture will have dried out and the tallow have struck well into the pores of the leather. No bad results will follow if the leather is allowed to remain a much longer time coated with the tallow.

After the leather has been in this state a sufficient length of time, each strap must be placed upon a bench, grain side down, and secured in the same manner as before mentioned ; then with a glass slicker rub the flesh side thoroughly, working in all the grease possible, the surplus being removed by the slicker. Then turn the strap over, and rub down the other side to set the grain and give it a fine appearance.

If the straps are to be worked up full, it will

not be necessary to rub the grain side much, as the rubbing incident to the process of fitting up will give it a fine finish. This recurrying is not done solely with a view of improving the appearance of the leather, though this alone would fully compensate the manufacturer for his trouble, the treatment being equally beneficial to its wearing qualities, as the leather is made more dense by the rubbing it receives, while the grease is worked thoroughly into every fibre, causing it to become soft and flexible.

With ordinary leather, this recurrying will reduce it in thickness nearly one third without a particle of its original substance being removed. The good effect is not so marked upon poorly-tanned leather as it is on that which is well tanned but poorly curried, but the improvement in the wearing qualities and appearance is sufficient to make it profitable to expend labor in this direction.

The leather used for single-strap track-harness should always be rubbed on the flesh side as has been directed, in order to give a fine, smooth, and perfect finish, which, after being blacked, will make the flesh nearly equal to the grain side. Besides this, the increased density given to the leather makes it possible to trim the edges smoothly and finish them as finely as the grain, and as this latter consideration is one of great importance to all who desire the harness to appear smooth and true, they will find it greatly to their advantage to follow the above directions when preparing their leather. Common harness could be made to appear much neater than is generally the case if the same course were followed in the treatment of the leather as recommended for fine grades, but as the prices are usually such as to render the carrying out of this system unprofitable, the leather can be fitted up without extra labor, the straps being moistened by dipping them into a pail of water, or by using a sponge. With this kind of stock, no more water should be used than is absolutely necessary to cause it to work up well.

CHAPTER VI.

A VERY large percentage of all the harness-makers in this country look upon the idea of measuring a horse as unworthy their consideration, but the experience and observation of the most enterprising men in the custom trade has convinced them that the reason why there are so many ill fitting harness in use is because of the failure of so large a number in the trade to adopt the same common-sense rules which govern other mechanics. There are some straps which can be lengthened or shortened to accommodate them to the size and form of the horse with out detriment; but the principal ones can not be so changed, and if not made of a proper length at first they seriously interfere with the appearance as well as the durability of the harness.

Prominent among the latter is the hame tug, whether it be for a short or long tug harness. If for a long tug, the length must be such that when the collar is well down upon the shoulder, the market tug will follow a line parallel with the center of the pad side: if this position is not maintained, an unnecessary strain is thrown upon the swivel, or loop in the end of the pad top, and the pad itself will be likely to be drawn out of shape and the appearance of the harness be marred. With short tugs the result is quite as injurious; if the tug is sufficiently long to allow the trace buckle to come in contact with the pad trace bearer on a double harness, and the buckle on the back band of a single harness, injury will be done to these straps, or to the hame tug itself. It naturally follows, therefore, that the length of the horse from the collar to the girth is an important consideration.

With breast collar harness the length of the body is equally as important as the length of the hame tug on the hame collar; the position of the neck strap tugs has much to do with the set of the collar and the wear of the harness. If the tugs are set too far back, the collar will sag in front so as to interfere with the movement of the horse, or it will be necessary to shorten the neck strap to such an extent that an undue strain will be thrown upon it at the neck strap tug when the trace is straightened.

The proper length for the breeching body, winker brace, cheek straps, girths, etc., are of equal importance; while the point of attaching the hip strap to the turnback, the front to the cheek pieces, and the position of the winkers, all contribute much to the durability as well as the appearance of the harness; yet there are those who ridicule the whole idea of measuring, they depending entirely upon lengthening or shortening such straps as can be adjusted by the use of buckles.

Manufacturers who carry on an extended business and ship goods to all parts of the country
can not measure every horse ; they have accord-
ingly adopted a set of lengths for each class,
based upon the size of horse upon which they are
to be used.

If a coach harness is to be made, it is supposed
to be for horses sixteen hands, or over, high, and
is cut to those lengths that experience has shown
to be the most correct for such sized animals.
If a double road harness is ordered, it is made
from lengths suitable for horses fifteen or fifteen
and a half hands high, while an order for a light
phaeton harness would be filled by cutting from
the scale of lengths adapted to horses fourteen or
fourteen and a half hands high. A light track
harness is cut to fit a horse fifteen or fifteen and
a half hands high, while one for a coupé would
be cut from the lengths suited to horses sixteen
to sixteen and a half hands high. Regular buggy
harness for common use are cut with traces and
other straps running lengthwise to fit horses fifteen hands high, but girths, etc., are cut for heavier animals.

The lengths used by these houses have been
determined by close observation, and are as
nearly correct as can be expected. Another rule
is based upon the lengths suited to a fifteen-hand
horse, adding or subtracting four inches to
girths, one and one half inches to breast and
breeching bodies, and three inches to hip and

COACH HARNESS.

neck straps, for every hand increase or decrease in the size of the horse.

Such tables are always valuable to harness-makers who are making up stock, and by a little observation may be made to answer perfectly for different localities ; but custom makers who do not possess these scales of lengths should measure the horses for which the harness is to be made if they hope to succeed in having it fit well.

In measuring for a bridle, ascertain the length from the corner of the mouth to one inch below the root of the ear, and add enough to this for the lap to secure the buckle to the top of the cheek piece, and also two thirds the original length : this will give a cheek piece long enough to allow the loose end to enter into the cheek loop about one half its length ; for the crown piece, measure from the root of the ear on one side, over the head to the root of the ear on the other side, and add five or six inches to each end for the cheek and throat latch billets ; for throat latch, measure from a point two inches below the root of the ear, around the throat, to the corresponding point on the other side ; for the neck strap to a breast collar, pass the measure over the neck just forward of the highest point of the withers, carrying the ends forward three inches to a point parallel with the point where the throat enters the breast ; determine the position of the tugs by measuring around the breast from the points designated by the ends of the neck strap. To determine the length of the breast collar, measure from a point four inches above the elbow on one side, around the breast just below where the throat enters the breast, to a corresponding point on the other side. The girth measure must also be taken.

If the harness is to be made up with a long tug and market tug, designate the exact location of the centre of the girth, and measure from the end of the hame draft eye to the point designated as the centre of the girth, and deduct from this the length of the buckle back of the centre of the loop. See that the collar sets well back in its place when measuring for the tug, as the proper length of this strap is of the greatest importance : if it is too long or too short, the market tug will not occupy its proper position, and thereby detract much from the appearance of the harness. In measuring for the breeching, draw the line around the buttock from a point just above the stifle to a corresponding position on the opposite side, and allow one inch for slack ; for hip straps, measure from a point ten inches forward of the crupper down to the point occupied by the body of the breeching, and deduct three inches for the breeching tugs.

The harness-maker who has a well-assorted table of lengths of the strapping for various kinds of harness need not measure the horse to be fitted except in special cases. A set of lengths which are suited to horses in one locality may be in part unsuited to those of another, owing to the difference in their build, and it would be well in all cases to test the lengths furnished before adopting them in full.

In preparing the tables of lengths and widths in this work, the author has aimed to secure those which have proved correct, and, while not claiming infallibility, he believes they are as near perfect as any tables of this kind can be. They represent a variety of styles suited to the wants of all classes of customers, and can be followed with safety.

CHAPTER VII.

No. 1.

SINGLE STRAP TRACK HARNESS.

BRIDLE.

	Length, inches.	Width, inches.
Crown	23	1
Cheeks	27	$\frac{1}{2}$
Throat latch	30	$\frac{1}{2}$
Front	21	$\frac{5}{8}$
Winker strap	12	1
Split	7	$\frac{3}{8}$
Billet	5	$\frac{1}{2}$
Half Kemble Jackson check	25	1
Split	12	$\frac{1}{2}$
Gag rein	24	$\frac{5}{8}$
Center piece	60	$\frac{5}{8}$
Billets	10	

SADDLE.

	Length, inches.	Width, inches.
Tree	3	
Flaps	$21\frac{1}{2}$	$2\frac{1}{2}$
Swell		$2\frac{3}{4}$
Points	9	$\frac{7}{8}$
Jockeys	$4\frac{1}{2}$	$2\frac{5}{8}$

	Length, inches.	Width, inches.
Belly band	18	$1\frac{3}{4}$
Chapes	7	$\frac{7}{8}$
Shaft girth	29	2
Billets	22	$\frac{7}{8}$
Back bands	20	$\frac{7}{8}$
Shaft tugs	18	$\frac{7}{8}$
Safety strap	45	1
Martingale, body	32	$1\frac{3}{8}$
Bottom lay	11	$\frac{5}{8}$
Ring piece, round	17	$\frac{7}{16}$

BREAST-COLLAR.

	Length, inches.	Width, inches.
Body	35	2
Neck piece	38	$1\frac{1}{4}$
Ends		$\frac{5}{8}$
Chapes	7	$\frac{5}{8}$
Traces	83	1
Lap, on breast collar	11	

BREECHING.

	Length, inches.	Width, inches.
Body	38	2
Layers	13	$1\frac{1}{8}$
Hip strap	43	$\frac{5}{8}$
Tugs, round	11	$\frac{7}{8}$
Chapes	7	$\frac{5}{8}$
Turnback	44	$1\frac{1}{4}, \frac{5}{8}$
Body		$1\frac{1}{4}$
Dock	14	$3\frac{1}{2}$
Reins	72	$\frac{7}{8}$
Hand parts	84	$1\frac{1}{4}$

Single Road Harness—One-Inch Trace.

BRIDLE.

	Length, inches.	Width, inches.
Crown layer	23	$\frac{5}{8}$
Cheek pieces	27	$\frac{1}{2}$
Winker strap	12	1
Billet	5	$\frac{1}{2}$
Split, flat	7	$\frac{3}{8}$
Winkers	$4\frac{1}{2}$	4
Front	21	$\frac{5}{8}$
Throat latch	30	$\frac{1}{2}$
Gag reins	24	$\frac{3}{4}$
Center piece	60	$\frac{1}{2}$
Billets	10	$\frac{1}{2}$

BREAST-COLLAR.

Layer and trace in one	89	1
Neck piece	48	$\frac{5}{8}$

SADDLE.

Tree	$2\frac{1}{2}$	
Flaps	$21\frac{1}{2}$	$1\frac{3}{4}$
Swell		2
Jockeys	$3\frac{3}{4}$	$1\frac{5}{8}$

	Length, inches.	Width, inches.
Points	12	$\frac{3}{4}$
Back bands	20	$\frac{7}{8}$
Shaft tugs	19	$\frac{7}{8}$
Belly band	22	$\frac{3}{4}$
Shaft girth	28	$\frac{3}{4}$
Billets	22	$\frac{3}{4}$
Martingale	41	$\frac{3}{4}$
Bottom lay	19	$\frac{3}{4}$

BREECHING.

	Length, inches.	Width, inches.
Breeching layer	45	$\frac{3}{4}$
Hip strap	45	$\frac{3}{8}$
Breeching tugs, round	11	$\frac{7}{8}$
Buckle chapes	7	$\frac{3}{8}$
Breeching straps	48	$\frac{3}{4}$
Turnback	44	$\frac{5}{8}$
Dock	15	3
Reins, flat	72	$\frac{7}{8}$
Hand parts	84	$1\frac{1}{4}$

FOLDS.

	Length, inches.	Width, inches.
Crown	11	$2\frac{3}{4}$
Breast collar	39	$3\frac{3}{4}$
Neck strap	26	$2\frac{3}{4}$
Belly band	16	3
Shaft girth	28	3
Martingale	32	$2\frac{3}{4}$
Breeching	36	$3\frac{1}{2}$

SINGLE HARNESS (BREAST COLLAR).

BRIDLE.

	Length, inches.	Width, inches.
Crown piece	23	$1\frac{1}{8}$
Billets	6	
Cheeks	29	$\frac{1}{2}$
Throat latch	28	$\frac{1}{2}$
Front, made up	12	$\frac{5}{8}$
Winkers	$4\frac{1}{2}$	$4\frac{3}{4}$
Winker brace	13	1
Billet	$5\frac{1}{2}$	$\frac{1}{2}$
Split, round	$7\frac{1}{2}$	
Checks	23	$\frac{3}{4}$
Billets	9	$\frac{3}{4}$
Center piece	60	$\frac{5}{8}$

BREAST-COLLAR.

	Length, inches.	Width, inches.
Body layer	44	$\frac{7}{8}$
at ends		1
Neck straps	40	$\frac{3}{4}$
at ends		$\frac{5}{8}$
Tugs	7	$\frac{5}{8}$
Traces	78	1

GIG SADDLE.

	Length, inches.	Width, inches.
Tree	3	
Flaps	$21\frac{1}{2}$	$2\frac{3}{4}$
Points	9	$\frac{3}{4}$
Jockeys	$3\frac{3}{4}$	$2\frac{5}{8}$
Back bands	21	I
Shaft tugs	21	I
Belly band	22	$\frac{3}{4}$
Shaft girth	28	$\frac{3}{4}$
Billets	20	$\frac{3}{4}$
Martingale	42	I
Bottom	19	$\frac{3}{4}$

BREECHING.

Body layer	46	$\frac{7}{8}$
Hip strap	44	$\frac{1}{2}$
Breeching tugs, round	II	$\frac{7}{8}$
Buckle chapes	7	$\frac{1}{2}$
Breeching straps	48	I
Turnback	44	$\frac{5}{8}$
Body		$1\frac{1}{4}$
Split	8	$\frac{3}{8}$
Crupper dock	$17\frac{1}{2}$	3

FOLDS.

Breast collar	36	3
Neck piece	24	$2\frac{3}{4}$
Breeching body	37	3
Belly band	17	$2\frac{3}{4}$
Shaft girth	28	$2\frac{3}{4}$
Martingale	34	$2\frac{1}{2}$

Single Harness (Hame Collar).

BRIDLE.

	Length, inches.	Width, inches.
Crown piece	23	$\frac{7}{8}$
Split	6	$\frac{5}{8}$
Cheeks	27	$\frac{5}{8}$
Throat latch	28	$\frac{5}{8}$
Front	21	$\frac{3}{4}$
Winker strap	12	$1\frac{1}{8}$
Billet	5	$\frac{5}{8}$
Split, rounded	7	
Check reins	23	$\frac{3}{4}$
Billets	$8\frac{1}{2}$	$\frac{3}{4}$
Center piece	60	$\frac{5}{8}$

HAMES, ETC.

	Length, inches.	Width, inches.
Hame tugs	13	$1\frac{1}{8}$
Hame straps, short	17	$\frac{5}{8}$
long	20	$\frac{5}{8}$
Traces	80	$1\frac{1}{8}$

GIG SADDLE.

	Length, inches.	Width, inches.
Tree	$3\frac{1}{2}$	
Flaps	20	$3\frac{1}{2}$

	Length, inches.	Width, inches.
Points	14	$\frac{7}{8}$
Back straps	20	I
Shaft tugs	20	I
Belly band	22	$\frac{7}{8}$
Shaft girth	30	$\frac{7}{8}$
Billets	22	$\frac{7}{8}$
Martingale	35	$\frac{7}{8}$
Bottom lay	19	$\frac{7}{8}$
Ring piece	20	$1\frac{1}{4}$
Split	16	

BREECHING.

Body	44	I
Breeching straps	49	I
Tugs	12	$\frac{3}{4}$
Hip strap	44	$\frac{3}{4}$
Turnback	44	$\frac{3}{4}$
at hip		$1\frac{1}{2}$
Crupper	18	3

FOLDS.

Crown	12	$2\frac{1}{2}$
Belly band	17	3
Shaft girth	28	3
Martingale	33	3
Breeching	37	$3\frac{1}{2}$

No. 5.

Heavy Coupé Harness.

BRIDLE.

	Length, inches.	Width, inches.
Crown	23	$1\frac{3}{8}$
Layer, cut to pattern	9	$1\frac{1}{2}$
Cheeks	30	$\frac{5}{8}$
Front	22	$1\frac{1}{4}$
Winker straps	13	$1\frac{1}{2}$
Billets	5	$\frac{5}{8}$
Split	$8\frac{1}{2}$	$\frac{1}{2}$
Winkers	6	$5\frac{1}{2}$
Nose piece	30	$1\frac{1}{4}$
Ends at cheeks		$\frac{5}{8}$
Throat latch	24	$\frac{5}{8}$
Round check	28	$\frac{7}{8}$
Billets	10	
Center check	72	$\frac{5}{8}$

SADDLE.

	Length, inches.	Width, inches.
Tree	4	
Flap	22	$3\frac{3}{4}$
Swell		4
Point	12	1
Jockey	5	$3\frac{1}{2}$
Back band (running)	46	$1\frac{1}{4}$
Shaft tugs	24	$1\frac{3}{8}$
Belly band	26	$1\frac{1}{4}$

	Length, inches.	Width, inches.
Shaft girth	30	1
Billets	23	1
Martingale	34	1
Bottom lay	21	$\frac{7}{8}$

HAMES, TRACES.

	Length, inches.	Width, inches.
Hames, 4 pounds		$\frac{3}{4}$
Hame tug, made up	$10\frac{1}{2}$	$1\frac{1}{4}$
Safes, full length		$2\frac{1}{2}$
Loops	$4\frac{1}{2}$	
Traces	72	$1\frac{1}{4}$

BREECHING.

	Length, inches.	Width, inches.
Body layer	52	$1\frac{1}{4}$
Hip straps	48	
Center		$1\frac{1}{4}$
Swell		2
Split	16	$\frac{3}{4}$
Tugs	11	$\frac{3}{4}$
Breeching strap	50	$\frac{7}{8}$
Turnback	60	$\frac{7}{8}$
Body	20	$1\frac{3}{4}$
Split	9	$\frac{3}{4}$
Dock	19	$3\frac{1}{2}$
Kidney strap	34	1
Ornament	$3\frac{1}{2}$	2

FOLDS.

	Length, inches.	Width, inches.
Breeching	46	$3\frac{3}{4}$
Belly band	17	$3\frac{1}{2}$
Shaft girth	19	$3\frac{1}{2}$

No. 6.
DOUBLE ROAD HARNESS, WITHOUT BREECHING.

BRIDLES.

	Length, inches.	Width, inches.
Crown pieces	23	1
Layer, waved	7	$\frac{5}{8}$
Cheeks	29	$\frac{1}{2}$
Gag runners	8	$\frac{1}{2}$
Throat latches	26	$\frac{3}{8}$
Winker straps	12	$1\frac{1}{2}$
Split	8	$\frac{3}{8}$
Billets		$\frac{1}{2}$
Winkers	$5\frac{1}{4}$	$4\frac{3}{4}$
Fronts	30	$\frac{5}{8}$
Checks	23	$\frac{3}{4}$
Center parts	60	$\frac{1}{2}$
Billets	10	

HAMES AND TRACES.

	Length, inches.	Width, inches.
Hames		$\frac{9}{16}$
Hame straps	24	$\frac{5}{8}$
Hame tugs		1
Safes	13	$1\frac{1}{2}$
Loops	$4\frac{3}{4}$	
Ends	$5\frac{1}{2}$	
Traces	80	1
Spread straps	18	$\frac{1}{2}$
Link		

PADS.

	Length, inches.	Width, inches.
Top	17	$1\frac{3}{8}$
Sides	18	$1\frac{1}{4}$
Points	8	$\frac{3}{4}$
Trace bearers	16	1

	Length, inches.	Width, inches.
Housings	24	$2\frac{3}{4}$
Belly bands	23	$\frac{7}{8}$
Turnback	44	$\frac{5}{8}$
Body		$1\frac{3}{8}$
Split	9	$\frac{3}{8}$
Docks	14	3
Standing martingales	64	$\frac{3}{4}$
Chin parts	12	$\frac{1}{2}$
Short reins, rounded	55	$1\frac{1}{8}$
Long reins, rounded	72	$1\frac{1}{8}$
Hand parts	102	$1\frac{1}{4}$

BREAST COLLARS FOR PATENT YOKE.

	Length, inches.	Width, inches.
Body layers	40	1
Loops	$4\frac{3}{4}$	1
Neck straps	43	$1\frac{1}{8}$
Split, long ends	$17\frac{1}{2}$	$\frac{1}{2}$
short ends	$14\frac{1}{2}$	$\frac{1}{2}$
Tugs, short	$2\frac{1}{4}$	$\frac{1}{2}$
Tugs, long	$2\frac{3}{4}$	$\frac{1}{2}$
Billets on yokes	6	$\frac{7}{8}$
Yoke straps	11	$1\frac{1}{8}$
Martingale	20	1
Billets	12	$\frac{3}{4}$
Safety straps	36	$\frac{5}{8}$

FOLDS.

	Length, inches.	Width, inches.
Belly bands	17	$3\frac{1}{2}$
Breast collars	41	4
Neck straps	8	4
Martingales	32	$3\frac{1}{2}$

No. 7.

SHORT TUG COACH HARNESS, WITHOUT BREECHING.

BRIDLES.

	Length, inches.	Width, inches.
Crown pieces	22	$1\frac{3}{8}$
Cheeks	28	$\frac{5}{8}$
Fronts, made up	13	$1\frac{1}{8}$
Throat latch	23	$\frac{5}{8}$
Winker brace	13	$1\frac{1}{4}$
Split, flat	8	$\frac{3}{8}$
Billet ends		$\frac{5}{8}$
Gag runners	8	$\frac{5}{8}$
Winkers	$5\frac{3}{4}$	$5\frac{1}{4}$
Cheek loops	$7\frac{1}{4}$	
Check reins	22	$\frac{13}{16}$
Center pieces	60	$\frac{5}{8}$

PADS.

	Length, inches.	Width, inches.
Tops	17	
At bilge		$2\frac{1}{4}$
Center		$1\frac{3}{8}$
Side pieces	26	$1\frac{3}{4}$
Trace bearers	16	$1\frac{1}{4}$
Lining	13	$1\frac{3}{8}$
Point	10	$\frac{7}{8}$

	Length, inches.	Width, inches.
Belly bands	24	$\frac{7}{8}$
Martingales	28	$\frac{3}{4}$
Bottoms	16	$\frac{5}{8}$
Billets	13	$\frac{3}{4}$
Standing martingales	60	$\frac{3}{4}$
Mouth pieces	17	$\frac{3}{4}$
Turnbacks	44	$\frac{7}{8}$
At docks		$1\frac{3}{4}$
Split	9	$\frac{1}{2}$
Hip straps	66	$\frac{3}{4}$
Dock	18	$2\frac{1}{2}$

HAMES AND TRACES.

	Length, inches.	Width, inches.
Hames		$\frac{5}{8}$
Hame tugs	16	$1\frac{1}{4}$
Bottoms	13	$2\frac{1}{2}$
Loops	$4\frac{5}{8}$	
Hame straps	28	$\frac{5}{8}$
Traces	81	$1\frac{1}{4}$
Spread straps	16	$\frac{5}{8}$

FOLDS.

	Length, inches.	Width, inches.
Belly bands	16	$3\frac{1}{2}$
Martingales	30	$3\frac{1}{2}$

No. 8.

Long Tug Coach Harness.

BRIDLES.

	Length, inches.	Width, inches.
Crown pieces	23	$1\frac{3}{8}$
Layers	9	
Cheeks	29	$\frac{3}{4}$
Face pieces	12	$\frac{3}{4}$
Ornaments	$4\frac{1}{4}$	2
Nose pieces	14	$1\frac{1}{4}$
Ends		$\frac{7}{8}$
Throat latches	26	$\frac{5}{8}$
Winkers	$6\frac{1}{8}$	$5\frac{1}{4}$
Checks for swivel	30	$\frac{7}{8}$
Plain	23	$\frac{7}{8}$
Crown piece billets	8	$\frac{3}{4}$
Center check*	60	$\frac{3}{4}$

HAMES AND TRACES.

	Length, inches.	Width, inches.
Hames		$\frac{3}{4}$
Hame tugs, made up	$16\frac{1}{2}$	$1\frac{1}{4}$
Safe		$2\frac{1}{2}$
Loops	8	
Traces	84	$1\frac{1}{4}$

PADS.

	Length, inches.	Width, inches.
Top	$16\frac{1}{2}$	
Center		$1\frac{3}{4}$
Swell		$2\frac{3}{4}$
Housings	$21\frac{1}{2}$	
Center		$3\frac{1}{2}$
Swell		5
Pad sides	26	$1\frac{7}{8}$
Points	10	1

* Other straps same as in No. 7.

	Length, inches.	Width, inches.
Market straps	20	1
Swell		$1\frac{1}{2}$
Market tugs	20	1
Loops		$4\frac{1}{2}$
Belly band, short	$23\frac{1}{2}$	$\frac{7}{8}$
long	35	
Martingales	27	$\frac{7}{8}$
Spread straps	18	$\frac{5}{8}$
Hame straps	28	$\frac{3}{4}$

BREECHINGS.

Layers	53	$1\frac{1}{4}$
Tugs	13	$\frac{3}{4}$
Loops	4	
Hip straps	27	
Centers		$1\frac{1}{2}$
Ornaments		$2\frac{1}{4}$
Split	19	$\frac{3}{4}$
Turnbacks	$32\frac{1}{2}$	$\frac{3}{4}$
Bodies	19	2
Layers	12	$\frac{3}{4}$
Crupper billets	8	$\frac{5}{8}$
Docks	$17\frac{1}{2}$	$3\frac{1}{2}$
Short reins	84	$1\frac{1}{8}$
Rounded	55	
Long reins	84	$1\frac{1}{8}$
Rounded	72	
Hand parts	108	$1\frac{1}{4}$

FOLDS.

Belly band, short	17	$3\frac{3}{4}$
long	20	
Martingales	32	$3\frac{1}{2}$
Breechings	48	4

English Four-in-Hand Harness.

BRIDLES.

	Length, inches.	Width, inches.
Crown pieces	23	$1\frac{3}{4}$
Chapes	2	$\frac{3}{4}$
Cheeks	$10\frac{1}{2}$	$\frac{3}{4}$
Billets	16	$\frac{3}{4}$
Throat latches	27	$\frac{3}{4}$
Nose bands, middle	$12\frac{1}{2}$	$1\frac{1}{4}$
Buckle-ends	13	$\frac{3}{4}$
Winker straps	14	$1\frac{1}{2}$
Split	$8\frac{1}{2}$	
Face pieces	13	
Fronts	13	$1\frac{3}{8}$
Winkers, square	$6\frac{1}{2}$	$6\frac{1}{2}$
Bearing reins	66	$\frac{3}{4}$
Round reins	$20\frac{1}{2}$	$1\frac{1}{8}$
Running bradoons	26	$1\frac{1}{8}$
Billets	9	$\frac{3}{4}$

PADS, ETC.

	Length, inches.	Width, inches.
Tops	17	
Bottoms	$21\frac{1}{2}$	$2\frac{1}{2}$
Point straps	8	$1\frac{1}{8}$
Girths	42	$2\frac{1}{2}$
Girth pieces	15	$2\frac{1}{2}$
Girth straps	16	$1\frac{1}{8}$
Tug belly bands	52	$1\frac{1}{8}$

BREECHINGS, ETC.

	Length, inches.	Width, inches.
Bodies	120	$1\frac{1}{2}$
Hip straps	48	$1\frac{1}{8}$

	Length, inches.	Width, inches.
Breeching tugs	13	$1\frac{1}{2}$
Trace bearers	18	$1\frac{1}{8}$
Turnbacks	45	$1\frac{1}{8}$
Layers	14	
Linings	59	$1\frac{1}{8}$
Cruppers	22	$1\frac{1}{8}$
Docks	16	3

TRACES, ETC.

	Length, inches.	Width, inches.
Traces, made up	78	$1\frac{1}{2}$
Draw leathers	8	$1\frac{1}{2}$
Hame tugs	$19\frac{1}{2}$	$1\frac{1}{2}$
Safes	22	3
At hame end		2
Short tugs	10	$1\frac{1}{8}$
Tug straps	18	$\frac{3}{4}$
Bearing martingales	54	$1\frac{1}{4}$
Short martingales	42	$1\frac{1}{4}$
Leader traces, made up	60	$1\frac{1}{8}$
Hame tugs	18	$1\frac{1}{8}$
Safes	$20\frac{1}{2}$	
All other leader strapping, narrower than wheelers		$\frac{1}{8}$

REINS.

	Length	Width, inches.
Wheeler	13 feet	$1\frac{1}{8}$
Couplings	9 "	$1\frac{1}{8}$
Billets	1 foot	$1\frac{1}{8}$
Hand parts	6 feet	$1\frac{1}{8}$
Leader reins	22 "	$1\frac{1}{8}$

TANDEM HARNESS.—LEAD-HORSE.

BRIDLE.

	Length, inches.	Width, inches.
Crown piece	23	$1\frac{1}{4}$
Layer	7	
Cheeks	29	$\frac{5}{8}$
Throat strap	26	$\frac{1}{2}$
Winker strap	12	$1\frac{1}{2}$
Split	8	
Winker	5	$5\frac{1}{2}$
Check for swivel	28	$\frac{3}{4}$
Billets	9	$\frac{3}{4}$
Front, made up	13	$\frac{7}{8}$
Center check	60	$\frac{5}{8}$
Reins	175	$\frac{7}{8}$

PAD AND LONG TUGS.

Top	17	$1\frac{3}{8}$
Housing	24	$3\frac{3}{4}$
Sides	17	$1\frac{1}{2}$
Points	12	$\frac{3}{4}$
Market tug chapes	20	$\frac{7}{8}$
Market tug billets	20	$\frac{7}{8}$
Belly band, fold	17	$3\frac{1}{2}$
Layer	23	$\frac{7}{8}$

	Length, inches.	Width, inches.
Turnback	44	$\frac{5}{8}$
Body		$1\frac{1}{2}$
Split	8	
Dock	12	3
Hame tugs	$16\frac{1}{2}$	$1\frac{1}{8}$
Traces	90	$1\frac{1}{8}$
Trace bearers	56	

GIG SADDLE AND SHORT TUGS.

Tree	4	
Flaps	22	$3\frac{1}{2}$
Points	10	$\frac{7}{8}$
Trace bearers	17	1
Hame tugs	13	$1\frac{1}{8}$
Traces	92	$1\frac{1}{8}$

SHAFT-HORSE.

Bridle cut $\frac{1}{8}$ of an inch heavier than that for lead-horse, the lengths being the same throughout.

SADDLE.

	Length, inches.	Width, inches.
Tree	5	
Flaps	23	$4\frac{1}{4}$
At swell		$5\frac{3}{4}$
Points	10	$1\frac{1}{8}$

All other parts cut to the same measurements as those of the Coupé harness, No. 5.

MEDIUM WEIGHT SINGLE EXPRESS HARNESS.

BRIDLE.

	Length, inches.	Width inches.
Crown piece	24	$1\frac{1}{2}$
Cheeks	30	$\frac{3}{4}$
Throat latch	22	$\frac{3}{4}$
Front	22	$\frac{7}{8}$
Winker brace	13	$1\frac{1}{4}$
Split	8	
Rounded	7	
Gag runners	16	$\frac{3}{8}$
Face pieces	26	$1\frac{1}{4}$
Split	10	
Check reins	22	1
Billets	10	$\frac{3}{4}$
Center	60	$\frac{5}{8}$
Winkers, square	5	

GIG SADDLE.

	Length, inches.	Width inches.
Tree	5	
Skirts, width to suit tree	22	
Points	12	$1\frac{1}{4}$
Belly band, fold	18	5

	Length, inches.	Width, inches.
Shaft girth, fold	22	5
Chapes	7	$1\frac{1}{4}$
Shaft tugs	20	$1\frac{1}{4}$
Billets	14	$1\frac{1}{4}$
Carriers for saddle	20	$1\frac{1}{4}$
Hame tugs	20	$1\frac{1}{2}$
Hame straps	20	$\frac{7}{8}$
Traces	74	$1\frac{1}{2}$

BREECHING.

	Length, inches.	Width, inches.
Body fold	38	5
Layer	46	$1\frac{1}{2}$
Breeching straps	48	$1\frac{1}{4}$
Tugs	12	1
Hip strap	44	2
Split	20	
Carrying straps	22	$\frac{3}{4}$
Turnback	44	1
Layer	9	
Crupper body	18	$1\frac{1}{2}$
Split	8	
Crupper dock	15	$2\frac{1}{2}$

HEAVY SINGLE EXPRESS HARNESS.

BRIDLE.

	Length, inches.	Width. inches,
Crown piece	22	$1\frac{1}{4}$
Cheeks	29	$\frac{3}{4}$
Throat latch	25	$\frac{3}{4}$
Front	30	1
Made up	12	
Winker strap	$12\frac{1}{2}$	$1\frac{1}{4}$
Split	$7\frac{1}{2}$	
Billet	5	$\frac{5}{8}$
Nose piece	13	$\frac{7}{8}$
Checks	23	$\frac{7}{8}$
Center piece	60	$\frac{5}{8}$
Winkers	$5\frac{1}{2}$	5

HAMES AND TRACES.

	Length, inches.	Width. inches,
Hames		$\frac{7}{8}$
Hame tugs	11	$1\frac{7}{8}$
Loops	4	
Traces	72	$1\frac{7}{8}$
Hame strap, long	23	1
short	17	1

SADDLE.

	Length, inches.	Width, inches.
Tree	6	
Flaps	22	$5\frac{1}{2}$
Jockies	6	$5\frac{1}{4}$
Points	10	$1\frac{1}{4}$
Back straps	22	$1\frac{1}{2}$
Shaft tugs	26	$1\frac{1}{2}$
Billets	14	$1\frac{1}{4}$
Chapes, long belly band	8	$1\frac{1}{4}$
short belly band	8	$1\frac{1}{4}$
Martingale	29	$1\frac{1}{4}$
Billet	14	1

BREECHING.

Layer	48	$1\frac{1}{2}$
Tugs	9	1
Hip straps	48	1
Turnback	46	$1\frac{1}{4}$
Dock	16	3
Breeching straps	58	$1\frac{1}{4}$
Reins		1

FOLDS.

Breeching	41	5
Belly band, short	17	$4\frac{1}{2}$
long	22	$4\frac{1}{2}$
Martingale	32	$4\frac{1}{2}$
Turnback	22	$2\frac{1}{4}$

LONG TUG TEAM HARNESS, SOFT PAD.

BRIDLES.

	Length, inches.	Width, inches.
Crown pieces	24	$1\frac{5}{8}$
Split	7	
Cheek billets		$\frac{7}{8}$
Throat latch billets		$\frac{3}{4}$
Cheeks	30	$\frac{7}{8}$
Fronts	24	$\frac{7}{8}$
fitted up	$16\frac{1}{2}$	
Winker straps	15	$1\frac{1}{2}$
rounded	9	
Face pieces	22	$1\frac{1}{8}$
Split	11	
Throat latches	24	$\frac{3}{4}$
Winkers	$5\frac{7}{8}$	$5\frac{1}{2}$
Inside checks	60	$\frac{3}{4}$
Outside checks	26	$\frac{3}{4}$
Billets	10	$\frac{3}{4}$

PADS, ETC.

	Length, inches.	Width, inches.
Tops	22	$1\frac{3}{4}$
Ends		$1\frac{1}{2}$
Ring pieces	26	$1\frac{1}{4}$
Center rounded	5	

	Length, inches.	Width, inches.
Nut pieces	18	$1\frac{3}{4}$
Skirt straps	32	$1\frac{1}{4}$
Back strap	60	$1\frac{3}{4}$
Split	52	
Chapes	9	$1\frac{3}{4}$
Layers	12	$1\frac{1}{4}$

BREECHING.

Folds	44	5
Layers	54	$1\frac{1}{4}$
Chapes for lead up	$6\frac{1}{2}$	
Layers	11	$\frac{7}{8}$
Side straps	68	1
Lazy straps	44	1

TRACES, ETC.

Traces, fitted up	72	$1\frac{3}{4}$
Hame tugs, fitted up	18	$1\frac{3}{4}$
Billets	16	$1\frac{1}{2}$
Belly band folds	18	$5\frac{1}{2}$
Chapes	7	$1\frac{1}{2}$
Pole straps	54	$1\frac{3}{4}$
Breast straps,	66	$1\frac{3}{4}$
Collar straps	32	1
Hame straps, bottom	26	1
top	28	1

No. 14.

Long Tug Farm Harness.

BRIDLES.

	Length, inches.	Width, inches.
Crown pieces	24	$1\frac{1}{4}$
Ends split	$7\frac{1}{2}$	$\frac{5}{8}$
Cheeks	17	$\frac{5}{8}$
Bit straps	$11\frac{1}{2}$	$\frac{5}{8}$
Throat latches, long	13	$\frac{5}{8}$
short	11	$\frac{5}{8}$
Winker straps	13	$1\frac{1}{4}$
Split, flat	8	$\frac{1}{2}$
round	8	$\frac{5}{8}$
Billet	5	$\frac{5}{8}$
Fronts	12	$1\frac{1}{4}$
Face pieces	22	1
Split	10	
rounded	7	
Checks	24	$\frac{7}{8}$
rounded	15	
Center	60	$\frac{5}{8}$
Billets		$8\frac{7}{8}$

PADS, TRACES, ETC.

	Length, inches.	Width, inches.
Pad tops, soft pad	36	$1\frac{1}{4}$
Layers	50	$1\frac{7}{8}$
Billets	16	$1\frac{1}{4}$
Belly band fold	21	5
Billets	14	$1\frac{1}{4}$
Hame tugs	17	$1\frac{1}{2}$
Traces	72	$1\frac{1}{2}$
Hame straps, long	22	1
short	20	1
Holdbacks	52	$1\frac{1}{2}$
Breast straps	52	$1\frac{1}{2}$
Turnbacks	36	1
Crupper bodies	17	$1\frac{1}{4}$
Docks	14	3
Billets		$\frac{5}{8}$
Lines		$\frac{7}{8}$
Billets	9	$\frac{7}{8}$

WAGON HARNESS WITH ADJUSTABLE TREES.

BRIDLES.

	Length, inches.	Width, inches.
Crown pieces	24	$1\frac{5}{8}$
Split at ends	6	$\frac{7}{8}$ and $\frac{3}{4}$
Cheeks	30	$\frac{7}{8}$
Throat latches, long	20	$\frac{3}{4}$
short	12	$\frac{3}{4}$
Fronts	22	$\frac{7}{8}$
Round reins	22	1
rounded	16	
Center pieces	60	$\frac{3}{4}$
Winker brace	11	1
Winker, wing pattern	7	4

PADS, ETC.

	Length, inches.	Width, inches.
Hame tugs	36	$1\frac{1}{2}$
With cockeyes and chains	76	
Adjustable trees, No. 6.		
Pad skirt	16	$3\frac{1}{2}$
Layer, also to line billets	20	$1\frac{1}{4}$
Billets	16	$1\frac{1}{4}$
Bottoms	18	6
Belly band folds	18	5
Chapes	7	$1\frac{1}{4}$
Billets	16	$1\frac{1}{4}$

BREECHING.

	Length, inches.	Width, inches.
Body folds........................	39	5
Layers........................	48	$1\frac{1}{4}$
Tugs........................	12	$\frac{7}{8}$
Side straps........................	72	$\frac{7}{8}$
Hip straps........................	26	$1\frac{3}{4}$
Split........................	20	
Crupper body........................	16	$1\frac{1}{2}$
Split........................	8	
Dock, folded..............	14	$2\frac{1}{2}$
Back straps, to sew in rump rings..	42	1
Breast straps........................	56	$1\frac{1}{2}$
Holdbacks........................	50	$1\frac{1}{4}$
Hame and carrying straps.........	22	$\frac{7}{8}$

TRIMMINGS.

2 pairs common low top wooden hames,
2 bits,
4 $1\frac{1}{2}$-inch cockeyes,
6 $1\frac{3}{4}$-inch breeching rings,
4 1-inch   "   "
4 $\frac{7}{8}$-inch   "   "
12 $1\frac{1}{4}$-inch buckles,
2 $1\frac{1}{2}$-inch   "
20 $\frac{7}{8}$-inch   "
16 $\frac{3}{4}$-inch   "
4 $1\frac{1}{2}$-inch trace buckles,
4 gag swivels.

Adjustable Pad Double Harness, to be used also as Single Harness.

BRIDLES.

	Length, inches.	Width, inches.
Crown piece....................	24	1¼
Split....................	7½	⅝
Cheek pieces....................	16	⅝
Bit straps....................	10	⅝
Fronts....................	22	1
Throat straps....................	20	⅝
Face pieces....................	23	1
Split....................	10½	
Winker braces....................	13	1
Split, rounded..........	7	
Winkers....................	4¾	4¼
Check reins....................	22	⅞
Center pieces....................	56	⅝

ADJUSTABLE PADS.

	Length, inches.	Width, inches.
Skirts....................	20	
Points....................	14	1
Pads....................	6	
Back bands....................	38	1

TRACES, ETC.

	Length, inches.	Width, inches.
Traces....................	78	1½
Hame tugs....................	10	1½
Belly bands, folded....................	19	3¾
Chapes....................	6	1

	Length, inches.	Width, inches.
Martingales, folded	30	3
Billets, collar	16	$\frac{7}{8}$
Points	10	$\frac{5}{8}$
Pole straps	48	$1\frac{1}{4}$
Yoke straps	48	$1\frac{1}{4}$

BREECHINGS.

	Length, inches.	Width, inches.
Body fold	39	$3\frac{3}{4}$
Layers	45	$1\frac{1}{8}$
Tugs, long	12	$\frac{5}{8}$
short	10	$\frac{5}{8}$
Hip straps	26	$\frac{5}{8}$
Back straps	36	$\frac{7}{8}$
Reins	78	$\frac{7}{8}$

TRIMMINGS.

2 pair low top wood hames,
2 adjustable trees,
4 $1\frac{1}{2}$-inch trace buckles,
4 $1\frac{1}{4}$-inch roller buckles—for breast and neck-straps,
14 1-inch buckles,
6 $\frac{7}{8}$-inch   "
24 $\frac{5}{8}$-inch   "
4 breeching rings,
8 $\frac{3}{4}$-inch rings.

PENNSYLVANIA WAGON HARNESS.

BRIDLES.

	Length, inches.	Width, inches.
Crown pieces	22	$1\frac{1}{4}$
Cheek pieces, long billet side	48	$1\frac{1}{4}$
short billet side	36	$1\frac{1}{4}$
Throat latch	39	$\frac{3}{4}$
Nose band	18	$1\frac{1}{8}$
Winker straps	12	$1\frac{1}{4}$
Split	9	
Front	26	$1\frac{1}{8}$
Winkers	$5\frac{1}{2}$	5
Check reins	78	1
Bit straps	12	$\frac{7}{8}$

BREECHING.

Butt pieces	56	4
Hip pieces	58	4
Cross pieces	62	$1\frac{1}{2}$
Side straps	54	$1\frac{1}{2}$
Braces	24	3
Hip straps	36	$1\frac{1}{2}$

	Length, inches.	Width, inches.
Back band........	46	4
Chapes....................	14	3
Short-top stay..............	8	$1\frac{1}{4}$
Back strap.......................	66	3
Split.....................	8	
Chapes, for square on rump.	8	2
Dock, folded.....................	15	$2\frac{1}{2}$
Belly band, long side..............	34	$1\frac{1}{2}$
Billet.....................	24	$1\frac{1}{2}$
Carrying straps.................	22	$\frac{7}{8}$
Hame straps.....................	22	$\frac{7}{8}$
Chain pipes.....................	30	5

TRIMMINGS.

2 pair hook hames, high top,
4 trace chains,
4 large rings, or D's, for breeching,
2 bits,
2 $1\frac{1}{2}$-inch buckles—breast strap,
2 triangles for rump,
6 $1\frac{1}{2}$-inch buckles,
2 $1\frac{1}{4}$-inch   "
16 $\frac{7}{8}$-inch   "
2 1-inch   "
4 $\frac{3}{4}$-inch   "

No. 18.

STAGE HARNESS.

BRIDLES.

	Length, inches.	Width, inches.
Crown pieces................	24	$1\frac{1}{2}$
Split......	7	
Cheeks.........................	30	$\frac{3}{4}$
Throat latches....................	22	$\frac{3}{4}$
Winker straps....................	13	$1\frac{1}{4}$
Split......	8	
Front...........................	22	$1\frac{1}{8}$
Made up......................	12	
Reins, in one piece...............	78	$\frac{3}{4}$

PADS, ETC.

Tops............................	36	$1\frac{3}{4}$
Points cut down to.............		$1\frac{1}{4}$
Tugs and belly band billets combined	30	$1\frac{1}{4}$
Center piece.......	9	1
Belly band folds.................	20	5
Chapes....-........	7	$1\frac{1}{4}$
Traces..........................	64	2
Stay loops, sewed in the trace......	12	$1\frac{1}{4}$
Breast straps.....................	56	$1\frac{1}{2}$

	Length, inches.	Width, inches.
Holdbacks........................	42	$1\frac{1}{4}$
Billets...................	15	$1\frac{1}{4}$
Collar straps.....................	30	1
Chapes...................	6	1
Hame straps....................	22	$\frac{7}{8}$
Carrying straps..................	22	$\frac{7}{8}$

BREECHINGS.

Folds............................	39	5
Layers........................	48	$1\frac{1}{4}$
Tugs............................	12	$\frac{7}{8}$
Breeching straps..................	72	$\frac{7}{8}$
Back straps, or turnbacks	56	$1\frac{1}{4}$
Crupper bodies....................	16	$1\frac{1}{2}$
Split.........................	8	
Dock, folds.......................	14	$2\frac{1}{2}$
Hip straps........................	30	$1\frac{3}{4}$
Split...................	20	

TRIMMINGS.

2 pairs high top Concord hames,
2 bridle bits,
2 pairs two-foot chains with D ends,
14 $1\frac{1}{4}$-inch buckles,
2 $1\frac{1}{2}$-inch   "
16 $\frac{7}{8}$-inch   "
2 1-inch   "
20 $\frac{3}{4}$-inch   "
6 $1\frac{3}{4}$-inch breeching rings,
6 $1\frac{1}{4}$-inch   "
4 1-inch   "
4 gag swivels.

No. 19.

Bitting Harness.

BRIDLE.

	Length, inches.	Width, inches.
Crown piece	24	2
Split	7	
Cheeks	13	1¼
Billets	9	1¼
Throat latch	22	¾
Front	24	1
Made up	12	
Throat latch	22	¾
Swivel strap	18	⅝
Gag rein, long side	66	⅞
rounded	16	
short side	24	⅞
rounded	16	
Side reins	42	12
Billets	9	
Martingale to buckle back	54	1¼
Split	15	
Surcingle, web	63	
padded	16	
Billets on broad web	24	1
Chapes	6	1

	Length, inches.	Width, inches.
Pad layer and billets................	18	1
Side chapes	21	1
Turnback, sewed in rump ring.......	42	1
Crupper body.....................	16	1½
Split....................	8	
Dock..............................	16	2⅛

TRIMMINGS.

1 bit,
2 martingale rings,
1 1¹-inch ring,
3 1⅛-inch rings,
5 1¼-inch buckles,
10 1-inch   "
3 ⅞-inch   "
5 ¾-inch   "

In making up, measure off 24 inches from the billet end of the web for the center of the pad, which should be 16 inches long; sew on the chape for the billet, and turn back the ring across the center of the pad; measure off from the center 22 inches on each side for the side check, chapes of ring, and buckles; buckle back the rump stay strap with a reverse buckle and slip loops.

Cart Harness.

BREECHING.

	Length, inches.	Width, inches.
Body	75	4
Layer, to extend to ring	64	2½
Hip strap	54	1¼
Tugs	14	1¼
Kidney strap	58	1¼
Tugs	14	1¼
Back strap	34	1½
Safe-piece	14	4
Layer or buckle piece	14	1½
Belly band, long	60	2½
Billet	24	2½

Bridle same as stage harness, No. 18.

TRIMMINGS.

1 saddle tree,
1 pair hook hames,
1 back chain,
2 holdback chains,
2 trace chains,
2 loop end pins for breeching,
1 2½-inch ring for rump,
4 1⅛-inch rings,
6 1-inch buckles,
8 ¾-inch   "
1 2½ inch buckle,
1 1½-inch   "
1 1¼-inch   "
1 plain ring bit.

MULE HARNESS.

BRIDLES.

	Length, inches.	Width, inches.
Crown pieces	24	$1\frac{1}{2}$
Split	7	
Cheeks	30	$\frac{7}{8}$
Throat latches	22	$\frac{3}{4}$
Winker straps	13	$1\frac{1}{4}$
Split	8	
Front	22	$1\frac{1}{8}$
Reins, in one piece	78	$\frac{3}{4}$

PADS.

Top	34	$1\frac{3}{4}$
Belly band folds	18	5
Chapes	7	$1\frac{1}{4}$
Hame tugs	32	$1\frac{1}{2}$
Breeching fold	34	5
Hip straps	24	$1\frac{3}{4}$
Split	18	
Side straps	62	$\frac{7}{8}$
Turnback	52	1

No. 22.

SHORT TUG BUTT CHAIN HARNESS.

	Length, inches.	Width, inches.
Hame tugs, to sew in side loops.....	36	$1\frac{1}{2}$
Short tugs for chains..............	52	$1\frac{1}{2}$
Pad fold.........................	20	6
Layer, to include billet linings	48	$1\frac{1}{4}$
Center lay for back strap..........	8	1
Bridle reins......................	78	$\frac{3}{4}$

All other parts the same as No. 16.

TRIMMINGS.

2 pairs of common high top hames,
2 common bits,
4 breeching loops for tugs,
2 pairs of butt chains,
6 $1\frac{3}{4}$-inch breeching rings,
4 1-inch   "   "
4 $\frac{7}{8}$-inch   "   "
12 $1\frac{1}{4}$-inch buckles,
2 $1\frac{1}{2}$-inch   "
20 $\frac{7}{8}$-inch   "
16 $\frac{3}{4}$-inch   "
4 $1\frac{1}{2}$-inch trace buckles.

Trimmings for Carriage-Harness.

No. 1.
Page 64.

2 1⅜ or 1½-inch terrets,
1 bolt-hook to match,
2 ⅞-inch shaft-tug buckles,
9 ½-inch buckles,
10 ⅝-inch "
6 ⅞-inch roller-buckles,
2 gag-swivels,
2 1¼-inch breeching-rings,
2 1¼-inch martingale-rings,
1 half-cheek trotting-snaffle,
2 ⅝-inch rings,
4 saddle-nails.

No. 2.
Page 66.

2 1¼-inch terrets,
1 No. 4 bolt-hook,
1 No. 2 fly terret,
1 front,
2 rosettes,
2 ⅞-inch shaft-tug buckles,
2 gag-swivels,
2 1¼-inch breeching-rings,
2 1¼-inch martingale-rings,

4 $\frac{7}{8}$-inch roller-buckles,
2 $\frac{7}{8}$-inch rein-buckles,
8 $\frac{1}{2}$-inch bridle-buckles,
3 $\frac{5}{8}$-inch buckles,
5 $\frac{3}{4}$-inch roller-buckles,
2 $\frac{3}{8}$-inch buckles,
2 $\frac{3}{4}$-inch rings,
1 half-cheek snaffle.

No. 3.
Page 68.

2 $1\frac{3}{8}$ or $1\frac{1}{2}$ inch terrets,
1 bolt-hook to match,
2 1-inch trace-buckles,
2 1-inch shaft-tug buckles,
9 $\frac{1}{2}$-inch buckles,
7 $\frac{3}{4}$-inch   "
5 $\frac{5}{8}$-inch   "
2 $\frac{7}{8}$-inch rein-buckles,
2 1-inch roller-buckles,
2 $1\frac{1}{4}$-inch martingale-rings,
2 $1\frac{1}{4}$-inch breeching-rings,
1 snaffle-bit,
2 gag-swivels,
2 $\frac{5}{8}$-inch rings,
4 saddle-nails.

No. 4.
Page 70.

1 pair $\frac{11}{16}$-inch hames,
2 $1\frac{1}{2}$ or $1\frac{5}{8}$-inch terrets,
1 bolt-hook to match,
2 $1\frac{1}{8}$-inch trace-buckles,

2 1-inch shafttug buckles,
4 $\frac{7}{8}$-inch roller-buckles,
3 $\frac{7}{8}$-inch buckles,
5 $\frac{3}{4}$-inch   "
12 $\frac{5}{8}$-inch   "
2 gag-swivels,
1 fly-terret,
2 1$\frac{3}{8}$-inch breeching-rings,
2 1$\frac{3}{8}$-inch martingale-rings,
2 rosettes,
1 snaffle-bit.

No. 5.

Page 72.

1 pair $\frac{3}{4}$-inch hames,
2 1$\frac{5}{8}$ or 1$\frac{3}{4}$ inch terrets,
1 bolt-hook to match,
1 fly-terret to match,
2 1$\frac{1}{4}$-inch trace-buckles,
2 1$\frac{1}{4}$-inch shaft-tug buckles,
4 $\frac{7}{8}$-inch roller-buckles,
2 1$\frac{1}{4}$-inch   "
1 $\frac{7}{8}$-inch buckle,
6 $\frac{3}{4}$-inch buckles,
11 $\frac{5}{8}$-inch   "
1 Hanoverian or scroll bit,
2 rosettes,
1 chain or link front,
2 gag-runners (hooks and eyes),
2 1$\frac{1}{2}$-inch breeching rings,
2 $\frac{5}{8}$-inch rings,
4 saddle-nails.

No. 6.
Page 74.

1 pair $\frac{9}{16}$-inch hames,
2 1¼ or 1⅜ inch terrets,
2 fly or post hooks to match,
2 fly-terrets,
4 1-inch trace-buckles,
8 pad-screws,
6 ¾-inch roller-buckles,
4 ⅝-inch   "
8 1-inch   "
2 ⅝-inch buckles,
2 ⅜-inch   "
24 ½-inch   "
4 ⅝-inch rings,
2 Hanoverian or snaffle bits,
2 hame-rings,
4 gag-runners.

No. 7.
Page 76.

1 pair ⅝-inch hames,
4 1⅝ or 1¾ inch terrets,
2 fly-hooks to match,
2 fly-terrets,
4 1¼-inch trace-buckles,
4 ⅞-inch roller-buckles,
4 ⅝-inch   "
2 ⅞-inch buckles,
4 ¾-inch   "
20 ⅝-inch   "

2 scroll or Hanoverian bits,
4 rosettes,
4 gag-runners,
2 hame-rings,
2 crupper-loops,
4 ⅝-inch rings,
8 pad-screws.

No. 8.
Page 78.

1 pair ¾-inch hames,
4 1⅝ or 1¾ inch terrets,
2 fly or post hooks,
2 fly-terrets,
4 1¼-inch center-bar loop trace-buckles,
4 1-inch tug-buckles,
8 ⅞-inch roller-buckles,
30 ¾-inch buckles,
8 ⅝-inch   "
4 ⅝-inch rings,
2 stiff scroll or Hanoverian bits,
2 Bradoon bits,
4 Bradoon swivels,
4 gag-swivels (hooks and links),
2 hame-rings,
12 pad-screws,
2 crupper-loops,
4 pad-loops.

Nos. 9 and 10.
Pages 80 and 82.

The trimmings for these harness are the same as for the regular sets of double or single, with the exception of the ring-rosettes for the bridles of the pole or shaft horses.

No. 11.
Page 84.

1 pair $\frac{7}{8}$-inch hames,
2 $1\frac{3}{4}$-inch terrets,
1 post or bolt hock to match,
1 fly-terret,
2 $1\frac{1}{2}$-inch trace-buckles,
2 $1\frac{1}{4}$-inch shaft-tug buckles,
6 $1\frac{1}{4}$-inch roller-buckles,
5 1-inch buckles,
1 $\frac{7}{8}$-inch roller-buckle,
14 $\frac{3}{4}$-inch buckles,
1 plain ring-bit,
2 rosettes,
2 gag-runners,
2 $1\frac{3}{8}$-inch breeching-rings,
2 martingale-rings,
1 plain front,
2 $\frac{3}{4}$-inch rings,
4 saddle-nails.

No. 12.
Page 86.

1 pair $\frac{7}{8}$-inch hames,
2 $1\frac{7}{8}$-inch terrets,
1 post or bolt hook,
1 fly-terret,
2 $1\frac{7}{8}$-inch trace-buckles,

2 1½-inch shaft-tug buckles,
6 1¼-inch roller-buckles,
4 1-inch buckles,
1 1-inch roller-buckle,
1 1¾-inch buckles,
1 ring-bit,
2 rosettes,
2 gag-runners,
2 1⅝-inch breeching-rings,
1 band-front,
4 saddle-nails.

CHAPTER VIII.

DIRECTIONS FOR MAKING UP A BREAST COLLAR SINGLE HARNESS.

THE man who performs his work well and quickly, possesses a capital which can always be invested to good advantage to himself and his employer; while the lack of the necessary skill and knowledge to accomplish these results acts as a serious drawback to success. In almost every factory there are those who, if they had received proper instruction when learning their trade, would have made first-class mechanics, but who, because of neglect on their own part, or on that of their instructors, lack confidence in themselves when brought in contact with others, and are content to hold secondary positions, passing through life without benefit to their profession or profit to themselves. Want of system is the great underlying fault, and is the principal reason why success is so seldom attained.

The journeyman who works at his bench in a careless, hap-hazard manner can not perform his part well, and is almost certain to interfere with the labor of those near him, while by his example he inculcates in the minds of the apprentices the same disregard for order and system as exhibited

BREAST COLLAR, SINGLE HARNESS.

by himself, thus working a permanent injury to all with whom he comes in contact.

There is on the part of mechanics a general disinclination to listen to advice based upon theory, and from a knowledge of this fact the author has prepared the following practical instructions in harness making in its various parts, believing the end sought could better be accomplished in this way than in any other. While it is not to be expected that the rules here laid down can be followed in every particular, it is believed that there is much that will be found instructive and useful even to the most experienced journeyman, and which if studied by the apprentice, or the journeyman who has been deprived of opportunities to learn his business in detail, will serve to advance them far more rapidly towards a mastery of their trade than if they depended solely upon the ideas and practices acquired at the work-bench.

The instructions given for making up a single harness will serve as a general guide which may be followed in almost every case, as they point out the routine to be followed and the manner of handling the stock.

To facilitate the execution of the labor and secure good results, the workman must so fit up the various parts that the stitcher can perform one class of work at a time; it will not do to call upon him to stitch a round, then a loop, followed by folds and other parts. As far as possible the rounds should be prepared at one time, the breeching, hip, turnback, and other plain straps at another, then the folds, loops, laps, and all other parts where there is any considerable work of a kind, each by themselves, not perhaps in the order named, but in such a manner that each particular class of work can be done without interfering with another. In the following instructions for fitting up a single harness, the rotation is such as to cause but little annoyance to the stitcher, while at the same time the fitter is not compelled to wait for any thing.

The plan here detailed is that followed in a factory where the leather is cut out and given to the fitter, and the stitching done by men who do nothing else. The leather being on the work-bench, the first act is to wet all the stock thoroughly in blood-warm water, but care must be taken to expose it to moisture long enough to draw the oil to the surface; then skive down all the straps or parts thereof that are to be made up into rounds, such as the winker brace, gag runners, center of breast collar, shaft tugs, and crupper dock. Slick them out and lay them aside to dry, then with a sharp spokeshave remove the flesh quite closely from the crown piece, check rein billets, belly band billets, center-piece, and cheeks; slick them out, apply a thick coat of clean tallow, and lay them aside to dry where they will not be exposed to the sun or to the heat from a stove, as such exposure will turn the stock dark and cause the tallow to spew. The fleshing is not necessary on fine stock, but

where it is requisite it should be done at this
time. Next skive the breeching, belly band,
breast collar, and neck piece layers, slick them
out and lay them aside to dry; then skive down
the trace fillings or raise to the required thickness, and take the edges down thin with a wide
edge tool. Next proceed to skive down the top
and bottom, and slick them out, after which raise
the top and paste in the filling (avoid using more
paste than is absolutely necessary), moisten the
top of the trace with a damp sponge and rub it
down with a bone, reverse the straps so that the
butts will run up on the outside and down on the
inside, then paste on the bottom, wet it in the
same manner as directed for the top, rub it down
with a bone, and then rub the trace well with a
rag: this will give the grain a fine, soft finish that
can not be secured in any other way. Then skive
down the tops and bottoms of the breeching
straps, slick them out, block, crease, and punch
holes in the bottom for the buckles; take the
edges down on the bottom to form the raise on
the top, raise the latter, and paste down for a
distance of four feet; skive the tops and bottoms
of the hip straps, slick them out, and take down
the edges of the bottoms to form the raise for the
tops; cut them off three feet eight inches long,
round the ends, paste on the tops, and rub them
with a bone and rag; lay them aside, and when
they are sufficiently dry so that the paste will not
move they are ready to sink, but do not dry them
in the sun or near the fire, as such heat will

harden the stock and cause the paste to dry un-
evenly.

Next fit up the shaft tug—eight inches for a
seven-eighth inch tug—the straps being cut one
and one eighth inches wide. Take off one eighth
of an inch on each edge of the portion to be
fitted up, raise and fill in the remaining portion
so as to take up the quarter inch that was trimmed off the outside, channel the inside so that the
stitches will be buried out of sight, and lay them
aside to dry. Now fit the dock, mark off and
cut it out, crease the edges with a fine crease,
prick off twelve inches, take the edges down
quite thin and bend the two together. Next fit
the rounds, commencing with those for the gag
runners and following with those for the throat
latch and breast collar. Take the edge off the
full length of the part to be rounded, and channel with a small round knife from the edge. The
gag runners for a half-inch bridle require to be
channeled four inches, the center-piece for a
breast collar four and one half inches, and the
throat latch sixteen inches ; hammer the straps
down, and fill them if they require it.

The winker brace is the next strap to be prepared. The billet is four and one half inches
long ; raise and crease it, hammer up the rounds
(which are seven and three quarter inches long),
line the billet, and allow the end of the lining to
enter the round one inch ; have the latter stitched, paste the billet down, and crease it when dry.
Next prepare the breeching tugs. The round

for the front one should be channeled three and three quarter inches, the back one four inches; black the part which passes around the rings, prick in the center, and tack in the rings. Follow these by the martingale. Mark off three quarters of an inch from the end to round in, then five inches for laps, channel seven inches, raise, crease, and black the laps; mark out, cut, and crease the layers; hammer up and fill the rounds, and have them stitched; then prick off the laps and have them stitched. Next fit up the turn-back. First mark off two inches for the laps on the ends of the dock billets; channel seven inches for the rounds; raise the laps, then mark off and cut out the wave, skive down the edges, hammer up the rounds, and fit the lining, allowing it to extend down so as to form the filling for the rounds; have the latter stitched, round them up, and paste up the turnback; when dry, mark off the wave the full length, and sink the crease for the stitching. Go over all lined straps and turn-back, after having marked off the wave or other pattern, with a sharp tickler, then heat the heavy sinker and finish the sinking. Slick the tallow off the crown and center pieces, cheeks, belly-band and check rein billets, and spokeshave the edges to clean them thoroughly. Then fit up the check reins, round the points of the billets, take a light edge off the flesh side, but do not disturb the grain; dampen the edges with a sponge and water, rub them with a bone until they are smooth, and, when dry, black, and rub them with prepared tallow, composed of one third part beeswax and two third parts pure beef tallow; rub them with a bone and then with a rag, so that the flesh side will be kept clean, crease the edges with a hot iron, crease and apply a little gum tragacanth (prepared by dissolving the gum in water and adding good black ink to give it color and preserve it), then rub with a bone.

Proceed in like manner to fit up and finish the centercheck, belly band billets, cheek billets, and crown-piece billets, after which prepare the stock for the round check reins. First measure off three inches for laps at billet ends, next fourteen inches for rounds, then four and one half inches for laps at rings, and three quarters of an inch to round in; cut the laps at the ring down to full one half inch in the center, and taper each way; leave the full substance where the leather turns round the rings, hammer up and fill the rounds, and have them stitched before fitting up the laps. Then mark off and cut out the patent leather winkers, frogs, etc. Scratch the lines for stitching, black over, and rub in a little tallow where scratched, and go over with a heavy sinker, which will tend to improve the appearance after the stitching is done. Paste up the winkers, but be careful to avoid wetting the patent leather, as the water will cause it to lose its fine gloss; stitch up the joining seam, leaving about three quarters of an inch on the top edge near the corner for the winker strap; apply a little paste to the inside of the winker plate, shove it in between the lining and the patent leather, and rub down on the outside with a gig or " jakee," then apply a little paste to the inside where it goes between the cheek straps, and tack down on a board to dry. When thoroughly dry, trim off with a knife and spokeshave the edges; dampen them with a sponge and rub with a bone, allowing the leather to become dry before blacking. After being blacked, tack the winker in its place between the cheek-straps. Next mark out by the patterns the layers for the breeching, breast collar, neck piece, belly bands, and crown piece, cut them out and take down the edges with a wide edge-tool, then spokeshave them to remove the ridges, wet and raise them on the raise block, rub off with a rag, crease with a double creaser, and then go over them with a sinker; when dry, black the edges and prick off. Cut out and raise the safes for the breast collars and belly bands, paste them on the folds, and when nearly dry double crease them ; prick off when dry, have them stitched and afterwards trim them off, wet all the folds, hammer them down, put in the filling, sew up, crease the edges, and tack them on the layers.

Finishing up the rounds is the next thing in order. Wet them and trim off the fillings, hammer down and pull them through the rounder, clean off with a spokeshave if necessary, black them, rub on a little tallow, pull them through the rounder again, and rub them down with a wooden rounder and a little gum. Wet the docks, hammer down the seams over a wire, stuff

with flaxseed, working it down with a wire, trim
the edge with an edge tool, black it, and rub
down with a wooden creaser to fit the seam;
bend the dock to the required shape, and lay it
aside to dry.

Next punch the breeching, hip straps, and
turnbacks, wet them, slick down the stitching
from the back side, and rub the tops with a rag;
crease the edges over with a hot iron creaser;
trim the projecting edges of the turnback lining
with a round knife, then take off a heavy edge
with a spokeshave, and trim with a straight knife
where it is necessary; dampen the edges with a
moist sponge, and rub smooth with a bone; when
dry, black them and rub on a little tallow,
after which rub with a bone and a rag, and finish
with a bone and a little gum. When the dock
becomes dry, polish it with a hot burnisher and
tack it on the turnback; have the laps stitched,
trim and finish them up. Then trim and finish
the shaft tugs, and polish the insides with a burnisher. Trim and finish the cheeks, put in the
winker brace and stitch it. Trim the traces,
punch and then wet them, slick them on the
back, hammer the edges down with a "snob" or
shoemaker's hammer, and square them with a
spokeshave; then with a heavy edge tool take the
edge off the top and bottom, spokeshave them,
trim the ends and around the dart holes with a
straight knife, dampen the edges and rub them
down with an awl handle (one that will fit the
trace); when dry, black the edges, rub on the tal-

low, and again rub with the awl handle; then rub off with a rag and afterwards with the awl handle and a little gum. Next finish the folds by wetting the backs with a moist sponge, then slick them down, wet the tops a little and rub them down with a rag, crease the edges of the layers with a hot creaser, and recrease the folds. This completes the harness in detail, and offers a perfectly accurate guide for a workman, whether working by himself or in a factory.

Uniformity can be obtained only by the use of good patterns, and it is to the interest of every harness maker that they be kept in good condition. To do this, cut them out of paper and paste them on thin, stiff patent leather, then, when the paste is dry, cut the leather to the shape of the paper patterns. All patterns for breechings, breast collars, neck pieces, belly bands, turnbacks, martingales, and crown pieces should be cut to the full length, and if cut at the same time to the required width it will obviate the necessity of moving them while marking off on the leather. The pattern for the trace wave should be cut one half the length of the trace.

CHAPTER IX.

THE single strap track harness owes its origin to the demand for a light, close-fitting, medium priced article for use on the trotting course. Originally the collar and traces only were made of single straps, the breeching and other parts being made in the usual manner. The superiority of this method of making the collar, however, soon became so apparent that the breechings and all other portions were made to correspond, and now few harness made up in other ways are used on the trotting tracks, while very many of this style can be seen upon trotters on the roads and pleasure drives, and so popular have they become that there are few sections of the country where they are not used to a greater or less extent.

Notwithstanding their being made up of single thickness of leather and in the plainest manner, the exercise of more than ordinary skill and attention is required to perfect them, as in their make-up they represent the minimum amount of weight, and yet must of necessity possess great strength. This result can be attained only by

HAME COLLAR, SINGLE HARNESS.

using leather of the best quality. Sides of uneven substance can not be employed to good advantage, owing to the fact that much of the strongest portion of the leather is necessarily wasted
in reducing all the straps to a uniform thickness.
Young steer-hides weighing about sixteen
pounds to the side are the best : they not only
give better satisfaction when made up, but they
are more economical, owing to the small amount
of waste incurred. But even with these sides
only the backs should be used, as strength is the
great end to be sought after.

Having selected a side possessing the requisite
qualifications, cut from the strongest portion the
traces and all other straps except those for the
breast collar, breeching, and bridle. These can
be cut from lighter sides, those weighing from ten
to twelve pounds being the best. When the
single strap harness were first manufactured the
breast collar and breeching bodies were cut from
regular weight stock, and the edges skived off
from the underside, but experience has shown
that lighter sides are much more suitable, the
leather being more pliant and stronger in proportion to its weight, the strapping when made
up sets closer to the horse, and the edges do not
roll after being in use for a short time. This latter qualification is of the greatest importance, and
should of itself cause the use of light leather.

When extra fine curried leather can not be
procured, well tanned stock, treated as has been
directed on page 55, will answer for all but the

finest grades, as it will possess the requisite
strength, and in many cases can be given a fine
finish. Let the leather be what it may, however,
the flesh side should be well cleaned off and
worked down with a slicker, as the slightest
roughness would detract from the appearance of
the harness, while adding to the possibility of
injury to the horse from chafing.

The most important parts of this harness are
shown by the sectional drawings on page 125. I
represents a section of the breast-collar, with
trace attached. The trace, A, is of single thickness; the lap on the body is eleven inches long,
cut as shown or to some other ornamental pattern. The ring to which the neck strap tug is
attached is placed five inches from the end of
the body; the trace is stitched on with from ten
to fourteen stitches to the inch according to the
grade of the harness. The neck strap tug is
quite short, and is provided with a three eighth
inch loop above the buckle, and a seven eighth
inch loop below. When made up to measure, the
tug is often dispensed with, the neck strap being
stitched to the ring, thus doing away with the
buckles. In the finer grades the traces and
bodies are neatly creased. The common qualities are in some instances made up without
creasing, while in others the imitation stitch
wheel is used for the purpose of ornamenting.
The latest freak is to mark off in the same manner as though the layers were full length, and to
lay up the ornaments in imitation of layers. The

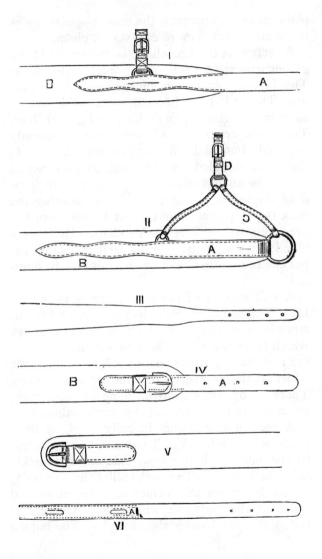

plain strap is, however, the most popular, looks the neatest, and is more easily kept clean.

A section of the breeching is shown by II, together with the breeching tug and buckle chape. The layer, A, is twelve inches long when made up. The end at the breeching ring is skived off so that the ring lap will be smooth and true. The tugs or braces, C, are most commonly rounded, but plain flat straps are also used; these are doubled and stitched, as they would neither be sufficiently strong nor keep their shape if of single thickness; the ring for securing the back tug is placed about eight inches from the breeching ring. The buckle chape, D, is provided with a loop over as well as below the buckle, though in cheap grades this may be omitted.

A half section of the neck strap is shown by III. This is cut of plain leather, the end is cut straight a distance of about six inches, above which there is a waved section five inches long, the remaining portion being straight, but a little wider at the centre than at the top of the wave. There is no stitching to be done on this strap, but a crease is run around it near the edge.

A section of the outside belly band, or shaft girth, is shown by IV. The billet, A, is stitched to the body with the flesh side out, the buckle being laid under between the billet and the body, B, so that when the former is wrapped around the shaft, the grain side will be out. One end of the short belly band is shown by V. The buckle

chape is stitched on far enough below end to allow the latter to act as a safe.   The safety-strap,
a most important feature of a harness of this
kind, is shown by VI.   It is in fact an extra back-
band, cut in one piece and placed over the saddle, with the ends buckled into the shaft tug
buckles or into extra shaft-tugs, the former,
however, being the most convenient form of at-
tachment.   The holes, A, are cut sufficiently
large to allow the rein terrets to pass through
them.   In some cases the safety-strap is made
up of a single thickness of leather throughout,
but in others a lining about twelve inches long is
stitched on to strengthen the strap at the terret-
holes.

The whiffletree ends of the traces are lined for
about one foot, or three or four inches more than
the space occupied by the dart-holes.   This is
generally done by turning back the extra stock,
the trace being cut the full length of the side.
Three dart holes are cut in, about two inches
apart, and the lined section, as well as the edges
of the dart-holes, are stitched.

The bridle used is generally a half-inch flat
strap with small square winkers and a full or half
Kemble Jackson check.   All the straps on the
harness require to be neatly rounded on the
edges, and blacked and finished on the flesh sides.

This harness is represented by Plate 1, engraved from a photograph of the celebrated trot-
ting-mare Goldsmith Maid.   The lengths and
widths for cutting are given in table No. 1.

CHAPTER X.

IN making up team-harness there is as good an opportunity for a workman to display genius in designing and skill in execution as there is in making the most elaborate coach or fine, light carriage harness. The difference, however, being that in the one skill in decorating as well as in finishing are the primary points to be considered, while in the other adaptability, strength, and fit are first to be secured, after which attention may be turned to finishing and trimming. The idea is by far too prevalent that it requires but little skill to make a farm harness, and unskilled, cheap workmen are employed who could not make up carriage harness of any kind. A good, careful mechanic will not only make the team harness better than the careless one, but he will, with no more expense, give it a much finer finish, thus producing a more salable and durable article.

In selecting stock, be governed by the directions laid down in Chapter I. Having chosen a side suitable for the weight of harness to be made, proceed to cut out the various straps by first straightening the back, and measuring off a strip from 18 to 20 inches wide ; draw a line with a straight edge, and cut the side in two

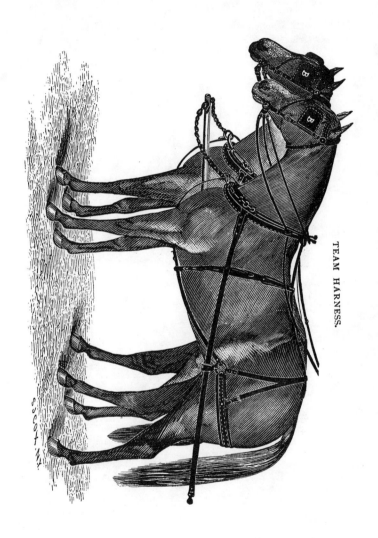

TEAM HARNESS.

pieces; the back will contain the heaviest and firmest part of the leather, the belly and flanks that which is softer and more uneven. Before cutting out the straps examine the grain as well as the flesh side carefully, to see that there are no cuts or imperfect spots; too much care can not be taken in this respect, as a blemish, no matter how slight, will show after the leather is wet up and while being worked. If the harness to be cut is a heavy one select a large spread side which will weigh from twenty to twenty-two pounds, cut the traces and all other straps which receive the strain, from the back, the folds, chapes, etc., from the belly part. The traces should be cut 76 inches long and 1¾ inches wide; if the leather is even and of suitable thickness, filling will not be necessary. The breast and pole straps should be cut next after the traces, the former 66 inches long and 1¾ inches wide, the latter 54 inches long and 1¾ inches wide. After the buckle is sewed on, slip on a ring for the collar-strap. Cut the collar strap 34 inches long and 1 inch wide. Use wrought-iron cockeyes for the traces, and in addition to the stitching secure each buckle and ring chape with copper rivets; these relieve the stitching from much of the strain that would otherwise be put upon it. Cut the hame tugs from heavy, even leather of equal strength with that used in the traces; they should be 18 inches long after being fitted up, and of the same width as the trace; the laps should not be less than 3 inches long. Use firm

leather for the loops, channel on the back to allow the stitches to sink below the surface, and
trim the edges a slight bevel. Cut the bottom
hame strap of good, firm leather, 26 inches long
and 1 inch wide; the top strap, 28 inches long and
1 inch wide, of strong but more pliable stock, as
it has to adjust itself to the shape of the top of
the collar pad.

Pads for these harness are made up in a variety
of ways, the old style soft pad being the most
desirable. Cut the top of good, even, and moderately heavy stock 22 inches long and 1¾ inches
wide, narrow the ends to 1½ inches, tapering up
3½ inches; cut the ring piece 26 inches long by
1¼ inches wide, and round up 5 inches in the center; fit the ring piece to the pad top with the
round well raised up, and place a martingale ring
under the round for a tie strap ring; then stitch
a ring on each end of the top. For the nut
pieces cut straps 18 inches long and 1¾ inches
wide, of heavy, firm stock. At the ends of the
round ring piece punch a hole for the pad-screw;
3½ inches from that point punch another for the
back-strap loop. To make a showy pad, use a
patent leather housing.

The breeching folds should be cut from the
smoothest part of the flank, and shaved down to
an even thickness. If the harness-maker will treat
the folds as directed in regard to rein leather, he
can produce a broken grain which will look much
better than the plain leather, and will not so readily show checks from use. Cut the fold forty-

four inches long and five inches wide. In all cases cut folds wider than the actual measurements, as the leather will narrow down in places while being worked ; they can be cut to the required width, when ready for fitting up. Cut canvas of the requisite width and fill in the folds ; coat the leather on the flesh side with tallow, and also apply warm tallow to the fillings. This will secure a durable job. Cut the back strap five feet long and one and a quarter inches wide; split it fifty two inches, leaving a short part uncut to wrap around the ring. If the leather is not heavy, use a wear leather where the back strap is attached to the hame rings. Stitch the hip straps to the rump rings before fitting up the buckle-piece. If a pad-safe is used under the rump ring, cut it half an inch wider than the rump strap, stitch it on with the edges even, and leave the swell end open, to permit its being stuffed with hair. For lead-ups for the breeching, use a six and one half inch chape of sufficient width for the buckle ; cut the layer eleven inches long and seven eighths of an inch wide, with a hole under the buckle for the hip strap points to pass through. Use one and three quarter rings for the breeching and one inch ring for the center lead up.

Cut the side straps from the center of the side, as it is necessary that they be of even thickness. These should be six feet long and one inch wide, leaving six inches for the turnback ; fit up with two loops, and use a snap and a slide loop to hold the latter to its place.

Make the belly bands of heavy folds, five and one half inches wide and eighteen inches long; lap the edges in the center, contracting the ends to the width of the buckle chapes; stitch through the center with one row.

The bridles, though plain, are a very important part of a harness of this kind, and the workman who slights them makes a great mistake. They need to be larger than other kinds, as the horses they are used upon are heavier. The fronts should be sufficiently long to allow the crown-pieces to lay one inch back of the root of the horses' ears. A short front will draw the crown-pieces forward and spoil the set of the bridle. Fifteen to sixteen inches should be the length used. The length of the crown is another important consideration; under no circumstances should it be less than twelve inches between the billet splits, the whole length being twenty-four inches. The cheeks should be seven eighths of an inch and throat latch three quarters of an inch wide. Cut the former thirty inches long; set the buckle above the winker. The winker braces should be cut fifteen inches long, rounded nine inches; cut the face piece twenty-one inches long, and split it ten and one half inches. All straps on the bridle other than the face and winker should be flat. Cut the inside checks sixty-one inches and outside checks twenty-six inches long, by three quarters of an inch wide; make up the outside with a ring for take-up. Use a plain leather winker, six by four and one half inches, with round corners and an oval end. These wear better and are less liable to be damaged than the square winkers.

Cut the lines from the best part of a side weighing about sixteen pounds; see that there are no cuts on the grain or flesh side. Make them up flat, about twenty-four feet long and one inch wide. The inside or cross lines must be six feet six inches long; billets, twelve inches long; finish off the ends with a billet in such a manner that a snap can be attached if desired.

The mountings, though of the plainest kind, must be strong, and in neglecting to procure those suited to the strain to be borne, harness-makers often· entail pecuniary loss upon themselves and injure their reputation. A weak buckle, ring, or hame, operates just as injuriously to the harness-maker as though the leather used was inferior in quality and the workmanship poor. The trace buckles are subjected to a severe test, and unless they are strong and perfect they will not sustain the heavy strain put upon them. There are a variety of patent trace buckles in the market, and, owing to strong competition, prices have been very much reduced, so that manufacturers have been tempted to make them much lighter than they should be. It is necessary, therefore, to examine them closely, and to buy the strongest and those most easily adjusted. The hames, which are of wood, should be strong and of good shape, provided with extra rings for split back strap and loose loops at the bottom. The small buckles should be strong and

of a good pattern—that is, so shaped that the
strap is not bent too much in passing through, and
the edges are not borne too heavily upon. The
common wire horseshoe buckle, which is used
more than any other, is the poorest article in the
market. The " Sensible" is a good buckle, and
there are others which answer quite as well, a full
description of which is given in the chapter on
harness mountings. But of all the buckles made,
there is none better than the large barrel roller-
buckle for a draft harness : this possesses great
strength, is easily loosened, and does not cut the
strap in the least.

The stitching throughout should be done with
white thread, as it is much stronger than black ;
it can be colored easily when blacking up for
finishing. Traces and tugs should have six or
seven stitches ; all other straps eight or ten to
the inch. Coarse stitching is the strongest, and
accords best with heavy harness.

The above instructions, though ostensibly for a
team harness, can be followed in a general way in
making up all kinds of draft harness. The following practical working guide will be understood
by the workman.

Before doing any thing toward fitting up, see
that every strap is cut and laid upon the work-
bench. First skive down all the folds, wet them
and slick them out, cut them to the required
lengths, and skive down and shape ends ; fold
them and hammer them down ; fill them with
canvas, felt, or leather, and sew them up ; then
shape up the chapes, skive down the ends, punch

the buckle-holes, and black and crease the edges; tack on the chapes and layers, and as soon as the leather is dry they can be stitched.

Before stitching the folds, wet all the stock, allow it to dry a little, then slick it out, point up the straps, take off the edges where it is necessary, and crease while damp. If the edges are rubbed down at the same time, they will finish better when dry; but the blacking must not be applied until after the leather is dry. If folded traces are used, mark a line in the center on the flesh side, and with a gouge take out about one half the thickness of the stock. This will prevent the leather cracking when being bent over. If doubled and stitched traces are used, paste up, tack, and crease them, and lay them one side to dry. Fit up the breeching tugs, turn four inches; use loops one eighth inch narrower than the tugs. Crease and stitch the winkers, put some paste on the plates, and shove them in; rub down with a round end slicker, and tack them on a board to dry. Fit up the winker brace, wet it thoroughly, and bend it like the letter B; tack it down, and allow it to dry before being stitched in. Make all the laps on the bridle two inches long; lap billets, three inches.

After all the straps are dry and stitched, trim the edges, using a spokeshave instead of glass to true them; black them, and then apply a little tallow and rub with a rag. Clean up the loops, and the harness will be ready to receive the final finish.

HEAVY ORNAMENTAL TRUCK HARNESS.

Among the many devices resorted to for the purpose of advertising a special business is the use of display teams, the harness for which is made in the most expensive manner; and it is no uncommon occurrence for a four-horse set to cost $2000, or a single set to cost $1200. As all these harness are made up in special styles, according to the taste of the party ordering them, a general description is all that is necessary.

The bridles are made up full coach style, the winkers square, with slightly-rounded corners; swivel gag runners are used, and the ornaments are alike on both sides; the cheeks, throat latches, and reins are cut three quarters of an inch wide; the winker braces are generally rounded; the face pieces are made with ornamental pendants, and are lined and stitched throughout. The entire bridle is fitted up with as much care as though designed for a coach harness. The metallic ornaments are of an appropriate design, to illustrate the business of the owner.

The wheel harness have no pads; the crupper or back straps extending forward to the top hand straps; the crupper bodies are made with wide scroll safes, padded; the layers, which extend the entire length of the safes, are cut to a suitable ornamental pattern, made up martingale fashion, lined and stitched with four rows, fourteen to sixteen to the inch.

The hip straps for each breeching are cut in one

piece, having a swell two and a half inches wide, the split ends being one inch wide; between the ends there are ornamental pendants, which are cut out of the same strap, fitted up quite full, and stitched with four rows, the center of the frog being provided with a metallic orna- ment; the hip straps are secured to the crupper body by metallic screws.

The breeching bodies are of solid leather, two and three quarter inches wide; the layer straight and stitched with four rows; the layers and hip straps are stitched fourteen to the inch; the tugs have full safes, with loops before and after the buckles; on each tug is an ivory ring in place of the ordinary breeching rings: they are put up the same as collar buckles, having loops for the tugs and trace bearer frogs, the latter being of some neat, appropriate pattern.

The breeching straps act as pole straps as well, as they extend from the breeching to the neck yoke, and are provided with heavy straps at the pole ends, and attached to the breeching martin- gale fashion.   Bearing straps are attached to the forward ends, and are secured to the harness by swivel snap hooks.

The traces and safes are cut in one piece, the safe end being four and one half, the other por- tion two inches wide, and attached to the harness by a heavy loop and three plated-head rivets; they have three straight rows of stitches, ten to the inch.

The lead harness, bridles, traces, and collars are

made up the same as those for the pole team, except that they are lighter ; they have, however,
pads, but no breeching. The former are of plain
leather, cut in one piece, with swelled sides doubled throughout and made very firm, the bearing
part lined and padded, and the tops stitched in
the same manner as the tops of coach pads. The
trace bearers are made heavy and strong, and in
addition to being stitched to the pad by four
rows they are each fastened by two pad-screws,
to which are fastened ivory rings ; rings are also
attached to the top in the center of each pad
through which the turnback passes to the hame
straps. The cruppers are made up in the same
manner as those of the pole harness, excepting
that they are provided with billets for the docks ;
the latter are extra large.

The loin straps are made up in the usual coach
style, with swell ends and hip ornaments and
trace bearers the same as those on the pole harness.

The mountings are generally silver-plated, all
the buckles being the "sunk bar." The round
reins are of russet, and the hand parts of heavy
buffed leather. The collars are heavy, having
piped throats, lined with thin harness leather.

CHAPTER XI.

FORMERLY every harness maker made up his own gig saddles, and any general information on that line of manufacture was of great value, but of late years a large percentage made are by parties who carry on the business of saddle making exclusively, or in connection with winkers, fronts, etc., and but few harness-makers can afford to make up the lower grades of saddles. There are those, however, who will not purchase ready-made saddles, and they would not think the manual complete without some instruction upon this very important branch of the harness business. To such the following plain details may prove of great value. The tree selected is the well known Tompkins, it being used more generally than any other.

The covering of the seat is the first part to be performed. To do this and make a perfect job, fit up the tree; for no matter how well it may have been made, there may be rough spots on the iron, and the wood in the cantle may need to be reduced in thickness. After having thoroughly cleaned the tree, unscrew the seat and remove it from the frame; varnish it with shellac varnish to prevent its rusting, or, better still, draw on a piece of sheepskin. When it is dry, proceed to prepare and draw on the seat leather, as follows : Cut a piece of patent collar leather, of the size required for the seat to be covered, dampen it with warm water, but do not wet the varnish and avoid using too much water ; stretch it to conform somewhat to the desired shape, put a tack on each side of the cantle, and clip the edges to admit of its being drawn down. Pull each way and cut off the surplus leather, then sew the parts underneath the seat with a cross stitch, after which pull up the cantle part and tack it all around to the wood. Cut a piece of leather of about the size and substance of the middle leather (this is to be removed when the jockeys are put on,) place it in position, and screw the seat to the frame in order to secure the seat leather firmly in its place ; use a washer temporarily until the seat is screwed on to remain ; then file off the projecting portion of the screw. When the seat leather becomes dry, put on the back pieces, draw the tacks from the cantle, cut off some of the surplus leather, dampen the part over the cantle edge, and with a pair of plyers set up the leather drawn over the cantle, clipping it where needed. Cut a piece of patent collar leather for the back piece of the cantle, of the same shape as the seat leather ; fit it nicely, and punch holes for the crupper loop, and cut apart from the hole to the bottom ; secure it in position by a few tacks, and prepare it for the binding. To do this, use a single thread

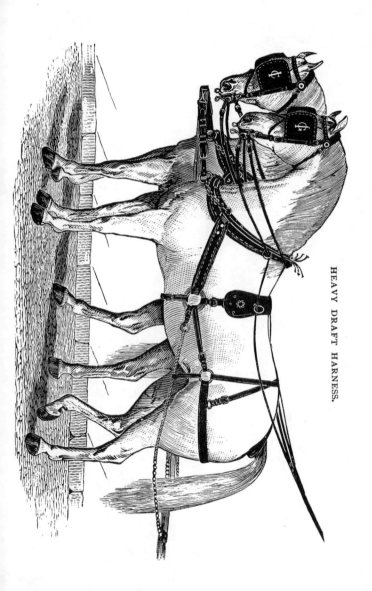

HEAVY DRAFT HARNESS.

carefully in such a manner that the stitches will not show through the binding, paste the two upper edges together, and hammer to make them firm and smooth. When dry, cut off the surplus leather, leaving just enough to form a binding-edge, and with a very sharp edge tool trim the back part, and it will be ready for the binding. To bind, cut a strip of enameled leather, about seven eighths or one inch wide (cutting parallel with the grain to prevent the varnish from cracking) and of the proper length, which can be ascertained by stretching it over the cantle edge; skin one side to a thin edge, paste, and with a slicker turn down the edge one quarter of an inch, rub it down and crease it for stitching; then draw it over the cantle, tack one end properly and carefully adjust it in its place until the circle is completed and the other end secured in the same way. Regulate it with a slicker (which should be about one inch wide to work well), after which allow it to dry, and stitch as neatly as possible; when stitched, slick, regulate, and trim off the binding on the back part, black the trimmed edge, and it will be ready for the jockeys.

To prepare the frame for the seat and jockeys, trim off the rough edges from the middle leather, cut two pieces of hard stock, about six inches long and of the same width as the depressions in the frame, skive down one end of each piece, and tack one in each of the depressions, with the skived ends toward the center; holes must be punched in them for the terret nuts, which should be secured with annealed or clout nails passed through the leather and clinched.

To make the jockeys, take a pattern of the required size, made of heavy leather or sheet iron, scribe and cut the jockeys, if for a covered seat, in two pieces; if for a japanned seat, in one piece; for a covered seat, skive the parts that meet on the center of the tree, dampen with water, and bend them to fit nicely over the seat. After stitching the jockeys, take off the edge with an edge tool, black, and rub smooth, and polish with a little ballblack. When they are ready, tack them to the middle leather on the frame in their proper place, screw on the seat, file off the screw if too long, wet the front and back edges of the seat leather, carefully draw it down, tack the front and rear, then trim off all surplus leather, and it is ready for the flaps.

The crupper loop should be covered before the seat and frame are put together. Cover it with plain or enameled leather, in the same manner as in covering a buckle or ring, and, when dry, stitch firm, trim off the edges, black, and rub smooth. To cut the flaps, patterns should be provided the same as for the jockeys; lay them on the leather, scribe around them with a round awl, and cut them out, true and smooth, with a sharp round knife; grease the under side with hard tallow, but do not allow it to touch the cut edges; immerse them in water for a few minutes, then lay them aside until the water has softened the leather enough for it to receive the crease-mark; a little grease applied to the glazed side will prevent the creaser scratching. After creasing, allow them to dry, then bevel and black the edges.

To flap off, cut the ends of the flaps to the requisite shape, so as to allow a portion to settle down in the depressions of the tree on the top of the stiffeners, leaving room for the back bands; fit the parts nicely, butting them against the crupper, so that the jockeys will hit the guide marks on the flaps; place them so that the tree is in the center, and nail through the holes in the frames, clinching the nails on a flat iron. The back bands being in their place on the flaps, adjust them on the tree, punch holes in them for the terret shanks, tack them fast, and secure the nuts with clout nails. After putting in the fore-piece, sew down the jockeys. If the flaps are lengthened in front, the forepiece can be dispensed with when making cheap saddles.

To make the leather loops, cut two pieces of thin harness leather, three and a half inches long and one and a quarter inches wide; also two other pieces of good leather, about as heavy as bridle leather, one inch wide by three and a quarter inches long; paste these on the thin, wide pieces, then cut four strips, a little more than one eighth of an inch wide, from the heaviest leather (as it is easier to paste before cutting); paste them three sixteenths of an inch from the outer edges, pat them down with a hammer, and allow the paste to dry; when dry, skive the ends, and they will be ready for the covering leather. Next cut a piece of good enameled leather of sufficient width to cover the body piece, shave down a little, slick out, cut in two pieces, paste them, and put them around the body piece; while damp, bind them over a piece of wood, three eighths of an inch thick on one edge, and, after adjusting them to suit the eye, tack them to dry; when dry, stitch them twenty to twenty-two stitches to the inch, and they will be ready to be put in the flaps.

To lay up the points for stitching, rough out the upper pieces eleven and a half inches long and three quarters of an inch wide, if for a three-inch saddle or under, of good but not heavy leather; cut the linings one and a half inches shorter and of lighter material; wet the leather as directed on page 54, and when partially dry it will work easily. If the upper pieces are not of uniform thickness, place the heaviest ends next to the flaps; slick them smooth, lay on the pattern, mark it, and cut out the ornamental section that is stitched on the flap; skive down the uppers on the flesh side where they lay on the flaps, leaving the edge the heaviest just at the end of the latter, as they are liable to break at this point if not well protected. Round the lower ends and skive them down a little on each edge; for a good job, make the two parts a little oval by bending them over the edge of a board, or by rubbing them down in a groove, crease the edge, and afterwards crease for the stitching. Skive the linings on the edges, paste them and the tops together, smooth with a rubbing-rag, and let them dry, then stitch from ten to sixteen stitches to the inch, according to quality. When stitched, dampen the leather a little, slick down the under side, and crease the edges again; trim them to the desired shape, black them, and rub smooth with a rag containing a little tallow, and with a stiff brush clean off the stitches. They will then be ready to attach to the flaps.

To make the back bands, rough them out to the required length and width, using the best quality of leather (the upper piece should be of good substance, but the lining may be of lighter stock); dampen them in the same manner as directed for the points, lay the upper pieces together, and mark off twelve inches for the points and one inch for rounding, if the parts above the points are to be ornamental; if not, round four and a half inches, leaving the remaining portion flat, to go under the jockeys and be secured by the terrets. The ornament above the loop should be made to correspond with the other ornamental work on the harness. Skive the edges of the under pieces, and cut the tops to the desired width, leaving them a little wider at the loops; sew the rounds where the loops are to go very strongly, round up smoothly, and paste the top and linings together in good order above and below the loop rounds (some prefer to paste up before sewing the rounds). Crease up for straight or ornamental stitching, whichever best suits the harness, and settle the mark for the stitches with a tickler. Where there is not enough substance to make a firm job, a middle piece can be used to advantage. Finish in the same manner as with the points.

To make the pad, cut the lining to the required shape, using the best English serge, and the body-piece of sheepskin or enamelled duck. If the former is used, it may be necessary to cut this piece a little smaller than when duck is employed, as it does not work up so much in sewing, and it is not necessary to take quite so deep a hold. Sew them together in the center with a few stitches on each side, to keep them in place, and scribe guide marks crosswise on the sheepskin or duck, to serve as guides for closing up the long cut after stuffing. Cut the facings of patent leather about one inch wide for all saddles under three inches, increasing the width for larger sizes. Be governed by the dimensions of the body piece in the length of the facings and fillings; the latter are preferably made of leather, but reeds are also used. In preparing the fillings, reduce them in the center at the hook, also at the ends, to make a good finish; baste the facings on the fillings with long stitches, having them a little damp. Sew them all together—the facings forming a welt, beginning at the center—with a strong thread, about four stitches to the inch; finish the ends neatly.

After sewing, cut the body piece lengthwise,

turn the pad, and sew together with a long loop-stitch ; the guide marks will assist materially in so joining that the original position is maintained ; regulate the facings while damp. If there be sufficient time, tack the pad out on a board in the shape to suit the flaps, and smooth the facings with a half round creaser, the same as for any rounded piece, and let it remain until thoroughly dry before stuffing. In making common saddles this may be omitted, the whole being worked dry ; but with a good saddle these points must be observed. Stuff from the centre with well-beaten hair, a little at a time, working it evenly into its place, and keeping it compact and smooth with a round awl ; after thus regulating it, quilt the pad up to the bearings, being careful to have each side correspond. Next sew the lining to the body piece, keeping the fulness of the lining drawn toward the lower ends of the pad ; stuff the bearings, and work with a round awl until the are sufficiently full, then with a proper tool pound the pad where it is quilted and stuffed, and it is ready for the saddle.

Before flapping, make the holes in the flaps for the loops, and prepare each of the latter for stitching. After the flapping is done, and before sewing down the jockeys, draw the loops in their places over the rounds of the back bands and down through the holes made for them in the flaps, pulling them tightly to their places, and tacking temporarily with small tacks ; sew them to correspond with the stitching on the jockeys, punch holes through the top ends of the back bands for the terrets, and nail them securely. Tacking is not absolutely necessary, but it serves to make a firmer job. After so doing, put in the terrets and hook, using annealed nails to secure the nuts, clinch them thoroughly, and sew down the jockeys. Trim up, regulate, and put in the pad, lace it thoroughly, clean off, and the saddle is finished.

Where a change is necessary in the shape of the flap, or larger or smaller patterns are desired, strike a line lengthwise through the center of the pattern, then take a pair of dividers and lay out the shape or size preferred, working from the center-line; when the shape is secured, cut one side, fold the pattern together, and cut the other. In this way a true pattern is obtained, while no changes are made in the part that fits the tree. Alter the patterns for the body and lining to correspond.

CHAPTER XII.

PADS FOR COACH AND TEAM HARNESS.

THE subdivision of labor and the improvements made during the past ten or fifteen years have, by making specialties of certain parts, such as pads, gig saddles, etc., taken some of the harness maker's work out of his hands, and enabled him to purchase ready-made articles at reduced prices, yet there are times when these must be made under the supervision of the manufacturer in order that they may correspond with all other portions of the harness.

Patent pads, which constitute the greater portion of those made up for the regular trade, are constructed in various ways, and as their manufacture is confined to the patentees, no advantage would accrue to the harness maker by a detailed description of the manner of putting them together. Instruction, therefore, in this respect will be confined to a few of the hand made pads which best represent their respective classes; more than this it would be useless to do, as the variety of style and processes of manufacture are so varied.

COACH AND CARRIAGE PADS.

By coach and carriage pads is meant all, whether light or heavy, that are designed for carriage harness in contradistinction to those used on team or draught harness. The process of manufacture is the same in all cases, whether the pad be light or heavy. Directions for making up will be confined to the pad, independent of the sides. The plates, which should be of wrought-iron, must be trued up, and the ends filed off thin and smooth. Cut out the top, punch the holes for the hook, terrets, and pad screws, blind stitch the ornamental portion, and stitch the pad plate lining to the top; trim off the edges to a sharp under bevel, then split the lining lengthwise, insert the plate, and whip stitch together with strong threads. Cut the socket piece of harness leather one half inch larger all around than the top ; the point, or pole, as it is sometimes called, should extend from $1\frac{1}{4}$ to $1\frac{3}{8}$ inches below the end of the plate; in cutting allow at least $\frac{2}{3}$ of an inch for fulness between the terret holes, and $\frac{1}{8}$ of an inch between the terret and pad screw holes. Skive off the edges on the flesh side quite thin, and back $\frac{1}{2}$ inch from the outer edge, punch holes for terret nuts, insert them, and rivet them in place ; in like manner insert the nuts for the pad screws, and screw them in position by means of a small cap piece stitched on. Screw in the pad hook, place the nut piece in position, and pound down enough on the pad screw nut to obtain the exact size, then remove the nut piece, and cut away for the pad hook nut; then place the nut piece in position, screw in the terrets, insert a short piece of harness leather the same width and thickness as the pad side, and set in the pad screw (be careful to set the mock side in proper position) ; then, with a hammer, set up the bolt piece to the plate, work in all the fulness, and turn up the edges square and smooth, and set the pad aside to dry. After the leather is dry, cut the pad filling out of heavy felt, paste it on, and, when dry, trim to the required shape. Cut the bottom from light collar leather, moisten it on the flesh side, work it up smooth, and paste to the edges of the nut piece; when dry, trim off flush with the top, skive the edges quite thin, and paste on the binding, being careful to work it up smooth and even ; when dry, stitch across the centre, leaving the gullet piece about $1\frac{1}{2}$ inches wide, then place the pad upon a block, and carefully stitch the binding ; trim the edge, and black if necessary. Pads put up in this way are firm, and much easier to make than those in which hair is used for stuffing.

The following directions apply to the manufacture of pads stuffed with hair. The routine for making is also somewhat different: Prepare the top and lining, and insert the plate as before directed, fit the hook and crupper loop in their proper places, bend the latter up so that it meets the edge of the top, fasten the screw or nut piece with a pad screw to the top, and force it up in the centre so as to obtain the requisite fulness, mark the holes for the screws and terrets, and also the outlines for the plate ; make the pole 1¼ inches long, remove the nut piece, and punch the burrow holes by the lower edges of the marks; this will secure the necessary fulness in the centre; skive off the edges of the nut piece, secure the burrs to it, and fit it up to the top with a hammer, being careful to turn the edges up true and smooth, and set it aside to dry; when partially dry, repeat the process so as to be sure that the edge is properly shaped ; do not remove the top until the nut piece is perfectly dry. Cut the bottom piece out of collar leather; to get the proper size, make a pattern of sheep-skin. This is done by dampening it very lightly, turning up the end around the gullet, tack it to the top, fit the other end around the pole, and tack it in like manner, then turn up the edge all around, and mark a line level with the top. This will give the exact shape without fulness. Remove this piece, and draw a line for the swell, the greatest fulness being opposite the centre of the terret holes ; taper gradually to the centre and ends, then cut the bottom piece to the new line by the pattern upon the leather for the bottom piece, and cut it out. Cut a small piece out of the centre in order to obtain fulness enough for the edges, whip together smoothly, turn the edges in the centre and fasten with a few stitches, draw the ends down and fasten the points with tacks, paste between the burrs and the lining on the edge, pop stitch together, leaving the ends open. Stitch across the centre, leaving a space $1\frac{1}{2}$ inches, paste the bottom to the edges of the nut piece, and, when dry, trim off to the required shape; paste the binding, and, when dry, stitch carefully; trim the binding close to the stitching, holding the knife so as to cut under in order to avoid showing a ragged edge. In stuffing, first work out the edge, then fill up the centre, tapering off gradually to the point; close the ends and tuft the point, and fit up to the top for the last time.

Fitting up the nut piece is the most important part of the work, and care must be taken to secure the requisite fulness to make a good job; also, to have the leather properly tempered so that it will retain the shape given it.

SOFT PAD.

A very large majority of the plainer lines of farm and team harness are made up with what is known as soft pads—that is, those without plates. The great number of styles makes it impossible, in a work of this kind, to give any more than a general notice, and as an illustration the one shown on page 154 is selected. It is one of the best, and embraces the general principles by which all soft pads are made. The tops and sides are cut of one piece of heavy harness leather, forty-four inches long; and, if designed for a one and three quarter trace harness, it is cut one and

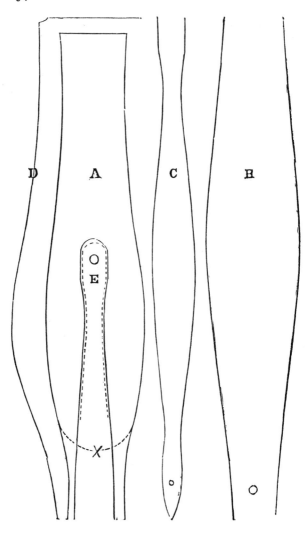

a quarter inches wide in the centre, two and a quarter inches at the pad bilge, two inches at the side bilge, one and a quarter inches at the narrowest point between the top and side bilges, and seven eighths of an inch at the bottom. Treat the leather the same as in making harness, and crease the edges with a double creaser.

The pad bottom is cut of good fold leather. In making the pad, cut a heavy piece of felt, nine inches long, for each side, of the same shape as the pad top, but about one quarter of an inch narrower. Cut extra pieces about five inches long to make the requisite fulness for the bilge of the pad ; cover the felt with the pad bottom, and lace the edges of the latter together on the top (the pad bottom should be wet while being worked, so that it can be fitted up to a good shape) ; then secure it to the top by a single line of stitches, or by binding with fancy colored leather, allowing the binding to terminate at the bottom of the pad, or to extend across the top in the form of a fold as shown by X, part A.

The pad trace bearer is shown by B ; its full length is nineteen inches, width at top three quarters of an inch, and at the bilge one and a quarter inches ; the upper end is attached to the pad top by a plated rivet, and stitched from four and a half to five inches from the end. The points are cut twelve inches wide and laid up on the pad side three inches, the lower ends of the trace bearers rest on the points and are stitched to them, one half inch bevelled plugs being placed between the two ; the whole is further strengthened by copper rivets. A ring for the back strap is attached to the centre of the pad by a chape stitched and riveted on.

This pad is sometimes made up with a short plate, extending down far enough to receive the pad trace bearer, a terret being used instead of the rivet ; when this is done, a loop check takes the place of the ring. The parts represented are : A, pad top section ; B, pad side section ; C, pad trace bearer ; D, one line of the pad bottom ; E, pad trace bearer in position.

PLAIN HARD PAD.

This, while being much firmer and stronger than the soft pad, is but little more difficult to make. It is designed for heavy wagon harness where terrets and hooks are to be used. A very good idea of its construction and appearance may be gathered from the illustration on page 157, which represents the various pieces drawn to one third their actual size.

The top, which is shown by section 1, is cut out of heavy patent or harness leather ; the openings show the positions of the pad screw and terret : this may be blind stitched if desired, but for general use it is quite as salable if left plain. If harness leather is used, trim the edges to a light oval and crease them with a fine creaser.

The bottom piece or lining is shown by section 2 ; this is cut of light harness or fold leather. The

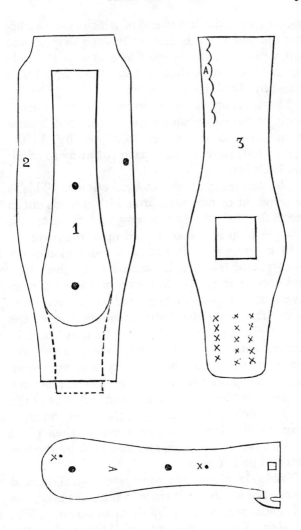

socket piece, the lower end of which is shown below the pad top 1, is cut to the same shape as the
top, a point a little below the centre of the hole
for the pad screw, then it takes the shape designated by the dotted lines.

The housing is shown by section 3. This is
made of patent leather with a scolloped border
bound around the edge, as shown by A; the
square hole showing the space cut away to admit
the back band.

The pad plate is shown by section 4. This is
of wrought or malleable iron with threads cut in
the holes for the pad screws and terrets; the
crupper loop is cast or forged upon the plate.

In making up this pad, cut the socket piece
from patent leather, the same size as the plate,
and secure it to the latter by means of copper
rivets at the points designated by X, section 4;
then draw over the bottom and tack it to the
socket piece, the nails clinching as they come in
contact with the plate ; lap the ends of the bottom so as to obviate the necessity of using a separate gullet piece ; then stuff the pad and place the
housing on the socket piece; tuft the ends of the
bottom socket and housing as shown by the cross
lines on the lower ends of 1 and 3 ; then place
the pad top in position, and secure it by the terrets and pad screws.

The side pieces are always cut straight and
creased or stitched ; if trace bearers are used, the
top ends are secured by the pad screws. The
housing is not a necessity with this pad, but it

makes it more ornamental, and is therefore preferred by most buyers.

Another style of pad which may be made up
with or without pad plates or stuffed pad, is made
by cutting a housing piece from heavy patent
leather to the required shape, and covering it
with soft collar leather. If no plate is used, the
back strap, which is perfectly straight and about
one and one quarter inches wide, is stitched to
the pad piece before the latter is covered; a
chape is attached to the centre for the back strap
ring, or a loop check hook may be used instead ;
four rivets, with round heads, are used to
strengthen the pad and to give it an ornamental
appearance.

A plain pad, which is used to a considerable extent in New-York upon team harness, is made of
two strips of harness leather ; one, forming the
pad and sides, is cut two and a quarter inches
wide and fifty-six inches long, the points one and
an eighth inches wide and ten inches long; the
layer is cut seventy-nine inches long and one and
an eighth inches wide ; this is stitched to the pad
twelve inches each side of the centre; the lower
ends are placed even with the bottom ends of the
points, and stitched to them and three inches up
on the sides, the fulness thus secured to the layer
makes it answer for a pad trace bearer; small
brass head rivets are placed in the centre of the
layer the whole length between the points at in-
tervals of about three inches.   The layer may be

left loose in the center, forming a loop for the
back band to pass through, or a billet and ring
may be attached instead. A thin pad, made of
two thicknesses of felt and fold or collar leather,
can be added if desired.

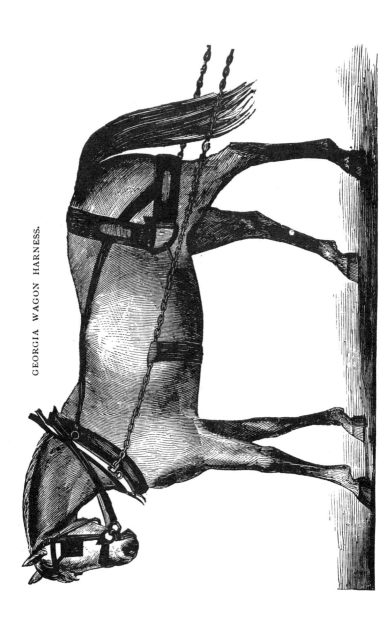

GEORGIA WAGON HARNESS.

CHAPTER XIII.

HARNESS MAKERS have three kinds of leather loops to select from—the hand made, patent, and pressed. The first are undoubtedly the best, and are used in preference to all others upon fine harness, some leading manufacturers using no other kind. Some makers of medium grades also use them to a considerable extent; but if well made they are too expensive for common work, and when poorly constructed are inferior to the other kinds.

Patent loops are made by being pressed up in hot dies, and are sold to the trade in every needed size and in a variety of styles. Being nicely finished and much cheaper than hand made loops, they have taken their place on medium grades, and are also used to a great extent upon common harness. Pressed loops are those made up in the workshop, and shaped by means of dies and presses after they are stitched upon the straps. The making of these and hand creased alone interest the workman, as the patent loops are ready for use at the time of purchase.

Hand made loops possess several advantages over other kinds; they are more durable, and, owing to the manner of making them, are less uniform in style of creasing than those made by dies.

Care in the selection of stock is the first requisite in making good loops, and the workman is referred to the description of the various qualities and kinds given on page 36. Next in importance is the tempering of the stock in water so as to bring it to a condition where it can be easily worked and yet retain the full impression of the creasing irons, which it will not do if either too wet or dry. The general rule is to soak the leather until thoroughly moistened, then remove it from the water, and allow it to become surface dry before creasing. Some workmen prefer to moisten the leather but a little before stitching on, and afterward temper it by the use of water and a sponge ; if, after being stitched on, the leather is found to be too dry to work well, the fault can be remedied by the use of a moist sponge. Owing, however, to the marked difference existing in the texture and fibre of each separate side of leather, and to the various portions of a single side, there can be no fixed rule given as to the preparation of it, and the workman must be governed solely by experience. As has been stated in another chapter, there are certain signs and indications which furnish an exact guide to the workman, but they are of a nature which can not be described, and it is his duty to pay strict attention to the minor details if he would meet with success in the leading features.

In order to secure a perfect-shaped loop, it is absolutely necessary to allow sufficient fulness in the leather to permit the corners being worked up full and square on the outside. To accomplish this, a fulness of about $\frac{3}{8}$ of an inch over and above the width of the loop stick should be allowed to a $1\frac{1}{4}$-inch loop of ordinary thickness, increasing or diminishing the same as the width or thickness is increased or diminished. This extra leather must be worked up and outward to the corners, so that when the loop is completed they are full and square, otherwise they will be thin and weak at the very point where the greatest strength is required

Hand creased loops are commonly attached by stitching both sides before creasing. Another method which is preferred by many workmen, as it obviates much of the difficulty arising from the leather becoming too dry before it can be creased, is the employment of a clamp in connection with the loop stick. When this is used, an iron loop stick is substituted for the wooden one. The back clamp iron is made the full length of the loop stick, and $\frac{1}{8}$ of an inch wider; at either end there is an ear, which projects about 1 inch above the back iron, the ends of which are bent over so as to cross the back iron at right angles; holes are drilled through the ends directly over the centre of the back iron: these are threaded and provided with a thumb screw. When used, the back iron is placed against the back of the strap, and the thumb

screws tightened against the loop stick, holding
the latter and the leather firmly together. In
securing the loop, one side is stitched in its
place and the other properly inserted, after
which the screws are applied and the whole held
in position until the loop is creased and finished,
after which it can be stitched fast.

If the ordinary loop stick is used, both sides
must be stitched fast before the stick is inserted,
care being taken to allow the requisite fulness.
First work up the sides with a slicker, then rub
down the top, and continue to work both sides
and top until the leather is pressed firmly
against the loop stick, always working toward
the corners to keep them full, then trim the
ends perfectly true, and run the edge creases
with a hot creaser, after which trace off the pattern and outline it with a fine tickler, then crease
up with suitable tools : these can be kept hot
and clean by laying the ends upon a metallic box
heated by gas jets or an alcohol lamp, the handles resting upon a wire support. The secret of
success in creasing loops is to define all corners
and outlines correctly before the leather becomes
too hard to receive an impression easily, the working up of the pattern afterwards being compara-
tively an easy matter. After the pattern is well
worked up, remove the loop stick and insert an
iron one which has been heated as hot as it can be
without danger of burning, then color the leather
with iron and vinegar black, and work over the
entire loop with warm creasers and slickers until

the leather is perfectly dry. By this process the surface will receive a fine polish, and if the color is good no further operation is needed. If a better black is required, allow the loop to remain unmolested until thoroughly seasoned, and apply a slight coat of hatter's black, and, when dry, polish with a silk rag. A loop which has been well worked will not be improved by the use of varnish of any kind. If the loop is properly made it will be solid and entirely free from grain cracks, the corners full and sharp, the ornament well raised and correctly defined. A soft loop is an evidence of a lack of skill, or of carelessness, upon the part of the workman, for if the leather is in proper condition and worked up as it should be, it will become firm and hard.

Pressed loops are the cheapest, and when well made appear nearly as well when new as the other styles. There has been a marked improvement in the manner of making them within a few years, and it is difficult, in some cases, to detect the difference between them and the patent loops. The same care is necessary in regard to providing fulness in the leather sufficient to produce square corners as is recommended in the case of hand made loops. They are needled on, and by the exercise of a little ingenuity the awl holes on the side last stitched may be so placed as to be almost undiscernable when the loop is fully pressed up. The machinery and appliances necessary for pressing up these loops consist of a good screw press, a metallic box with open ends, the sides being about 3 inches high on the inside, and the width for other than pressing cheek loops 3 inches wide in the clear ; for cheek loops a box fully wide enough to admit the winker is necessary ; in one side of the box place two thumb screws about $1\frac{1}{2}$ inches from the bottom, one within 2 inches of each end ; in addition small side plates are needed to be placed between the sides of the box and the loop, also plates to be placed upon the bottom for raising or lowering the loop according to its thickness ; iron loop sticks, and the top stamps or dies. In pressing, the loop stick is placed in its proper position, the strap laid in the box, and the side screws tightened up until the leather is pressed firmly against the sides of the loop stick, after which the die is placed in position and the screw pressure applied to the top. It is necessary to screw the side plates well up or the heavy pressure on the top will cause the loop to spread on the top edge. Two minutes under the press is all that is necessary to secure a firm loop even with cold irons. By the exercise of a little ingenuity in designing dies, a variety of patterns may be produced and cheap harness relieved of the sameness now so prevalent. With pressed as with other loops, much of the success in their production depends upon the leather being properly tempered. After the loop is seasoned, color it with vinegar and iron black, and when dry rub

with a woolen cloth, after which it may be finished the same as hand made loops. By the use
of a box of this kind, together with dies, small
loops may be made similar to the patent ones,
and of patterns to match the large ones.

CHAPTER XIV.

IN stitching harness two objects are to be attained—strength and ornamentation. The first is secured by the use of thread of the required size to suit the work to be done, making it up properly, employing an awl that is neither too large nor too small, and drawing the work well together. The second, by laying the stitches in an artistic manner so that, when the work is finished, the lines of the pattern are well maintained and the stitches of a uniform length and laid true.

The first point to be considered is the selection of the linen thread or silk, and the proper manner of making up the strand. Thread as now sold in the market is designated by numbers; the sizes used by harness makers are Nos. 0, 10, 3, 12, and 5, the latter being the finest used; Nos. 6 and 19 are of the same size, but of different colors, 5 being black, 6 white, and 19 yellow. These sizes should be used in such a manner as to secure the greatest strength. The rule adopted is to grade the thread according to the number of stitches to be employed. No. 0, which is the coarsest, should be made up with four strands, and be used where the stitches number eight or under to the inch; No. 10 is a little lighter than No. 0, and is used in the lightest work; where the stitching is not more than ten nor less than eight to the inch, three strands are used. No. 3 is also used where the stitching ranges from eight to ten to the inch, it being finer than either 10 or 0; four strands are required for all ordinary work; for ten to sixteen to the inch No. 12 is used, four strands being required. When the stitching is as fine as eighteen to the inch the same number is used, but only three strands; for all work finer than eighteen stitches No. 5 is the only thread used; this is made up with three or four strands, according to the character of the work to be done. These numbers represent the ball thread; skein thread, however, varies but little in size with corresponding numbers, but, owing to its being smoother, it appears finer. For all heavy work the ball thread answers equally as well as the skein; but in making up, the thread, while being twisted, should be well rubbed with the awl handle in order to remove the irregularities. Where the work to be done is fine and first-class in every respect, use the skein thread. White thread is preferred, by harness-makers who have tested its merit, on heavy stitching, owing to its possessing greater strength than the colored.

Having selected the requisite number of thread, the next thing is to break off the strands, wax and twist them up; unless this is well done the work will prove a failure. In running off each strand, it should be examined to prevent any hard, irregular spot being twisted up in the thread; in most cases the little lumps which are found are loose and can be removed without injuring the thread; where this can not be done, break it off and start anew. For stitching all articles like traces or other long straps, long threads are desirable in order to avoid starting with a new thread in the body of the work. Ten to eleven feet, however, is as great a length as can be used to advantage, and even this is liable to become weakened by the constant wear before being used up. In making a thread, untwist and pull apart the strand at the end, throw the center over a hook, and untwist and pull apart for the first strand; repeat this operation until the required number of strands are obtained. Untwisting before breaking the thread is a matter of much more importance than is generally supposed. If carefully done, the fibres are separated but not broken, and a smooth, regular, tapered end can be obtained; but if broken off, the end will be irregular and cause annoyance in threading the needles or attaching the bristles.

There is much difference of opinion as to the manner of waxing; some claim that no wax should be used until the strands are well twisted together, then they should be rubbed until the thread is well filled, after which it should be rubbed with a cloth to remove all surplus wax.

Others claim that the principal part of the waxing should be done before twisting, and that the only benefit derived from using wax on the surface is to preserve the thread from injury by the friction occasioned by drawing it through the holes in the leather. A careful examination of the thread after having been used in stitching, would seem to give support to the latter method of making up, as it is found, upon cutting apart, that the amount of wax left on the surface is so small as to preclude the idea of its being any advantage either as to strength or resistance to the action of water, while strands which had been well waxed before twisting retained all but the surface wax. Fine threads may be made up according to the first plan, but all heavy threads should be well waxed before twisting.

After the strands are all broken off, rub them well by giving one turn around the awl handle and rubbing it back and forth, then apply the wax, and twist up moderately firm. A thread may be injured by twisting too firmly as well as by leaving it loose. In the first instance it will not take the wax well and wears away rapidly; in the second, the strands are likely to open and show after the stitch is laid. The workman must therefore depend upon his own judgment as to the proper amount of twist to be given. The best is the ordinary shoemaker's black wax, which is made of equal parts of pitch and tallow, and is a good wax for general use; but this is too hard for winter, when a larger percentage of tallow is required, making the proportions one pound of tallow to three quarters of a pound of pitch. Various degrees of hardness may be obtained by changing the proportions. This, however, will not answer for white or light-colored thread. A good wax for this purpose can be made of refined pitch and tallow, the proportions to be governed by the degree of hardness desired. Ordinary yellow and white wax are also used for light thread, but they are not as good as that made of pitch.

Stitching, to appear well, must be regular, each stitch being full, defined, and of equal length. The use of the prick wheel assists materially toward producing the last result, but unless the workman handles his awl correctly irregularities will occur. Tastes differ as to the best position for the stitches. There was a time when straight stitching was ignored by all leading manufacturers on account of its resemblance to machine work, but the improvements in the latter soon made it possible to imitate any hand stitch, and the straight stitch has once more become popular. The custom now practiced by leading manufacturers is to lay all heavy stitches ten or less to the inch at a moderate angle, using a diamond-shaped awl; to secure uniformity the awl is held in a position which brings a face of the angle on a line parallel with the top of the jaw of the stitching-horse; to render this result certain, a portion of the handle is flattened to correspond with the angle on the awl. If the stitching is sixtcen or less to the inch, the angle is reduced, but the same precaution is taken to secure regularity. All stitches where there are more than sixteen to the inch, are laid straight.

The manner of drawing up the stitches has much to do with their uniformity : drawing harder on one thread than on the other will produce irregularity. A common fault with stitchers is to tighten the thread with one motion as soon as it becomes short enough for them to do so ; this is a serious fault, as it is impossible to lay the stitches even. No matter what the length of the thread, the tightening up should always be a distinct motion. If the stitches are to be flat, the force applied to both threads should be equal; but if a full stitch is desired on the face side, the thread bearing against the under side should be drawn the tightest ; care must be taken not to draw upon this thread enough to draw out the channeling. Stitchers are apt to draw the thread in the awl hand the tightest, and it requires some practice to overcome this difficulty.

When performing a piece of work where the stitches are equally exposed from both sides, it is necessary to change the position of the thread on the side opposite the awl hand, or the work will be irregular, and it will be an easy matter to determine which is the right side. To do this work properly, enter the needles, and when that on the left side is drawn nearly out, bring the loose thread forward, and throw it over the needle, and tighten up in the usual manner.

If care is taken to throw the thread over, the work will appear nearly as well upon the reverse as upon the right side.

The points to be observed, therefore, are : to drive the awl through at right angles with the face of the leather, holding it so that it will always enter the leather in the same position ; to draw the threads carefully, so that each stitch is set in at a uniform depth, and the fulness retained on the outside. When the work is well fitted up, it will not require much power to set the stitches correctly. Around buckles, when the laps have not been previously worked together, it will require more force to draw the straps together ; but under no circumstance should the stitches be buried into the leather, as this has a tendency to weaken rather than strengthen the work.

CHAPTER XV.

MAKING ROUND REINS.

THE very general use of round reins and their effect upon the appearance of the harness render it necessary that the most approved manner of making up be thoroughly understood, and entitle this branch of harness making to a separate notice. In preparing the following instructions, the grade of round russet reins known as No. 4 has been selected as the one embracing the various manipulations more thoroughly than any other, covering as it does all the essential points.

Good stock is indispensable to success, and care should be taken to secure smooth, fine-grained, and well tanned rein leather, the different qualities of which are clearly described in the chapter on " Russet Leather," page 33. Cut the leather seven eighths of an inch wide, and of the full length of the side ; soak it in clean water for a few minutes, and remove a thin shaving from the flesh side ; then lay it out straight upon the board, grain side down, moisten slightly with a sponge and clean water, and shave down to the required thickness ; slick down nicely while the leather is damp, and measure off five inches from one end for the billet and stop, and five feet six inches from this point for the round, with an additional five and a quarter inches for the hand-part lap. Measure off on the rein seven eighths or three quarters of an inch, or whatever size may be necessary, for the billet ; lay the rein out on the board with the grain side up, secure it firmly with awls, and with a channeling tool, held firmly in the hand, channel the five feet six inches which are to be rounded ; trim each edge with an edge tool, as by so doing considerable work, that would otherwise have to be done with the spokeshave, can be saved and a better job produced. Cut the width of the billet—which is five inches—on the edge of the rein, edge it with a small edge tool, stain and rub the edges until a good polish is produced, then with a seven-eighth inch buckle punch make the hole for the buckle about three inches from the end, and with a round knife trim down nearly to a feather edge ; turn the rein about, and stamp with a die, or mark off to a suitable pattern—four waves running to a point is a good one—stain the edges, and rub them well, then with a wide edge tool trim them slanting, so as to leave a raise in the center. Both sides being finished as directed, dampen the leather with a moist sponge, and with a raising block raise the handpart end light-ly ; if raised too much, rub down with a clean piece of paper, then with a double creaser sink the creases well, and prick off with a No. 14 prick-wheel, after which rub the edges smooth.

The rein is now ready for the stop, which is made of two pieces of clean stock dampened and shaved down to the required thickness, then pasted together and allowed to dry ; when perfectly dry, cut out with a die, or to a pattern, an egg-shaped or other design ; stitch the stop, trim off the back edge with an edge tool, dampen the edges lightly, apply the stain, and rub until a good smooth surface and polish are produced. Heat a narrow iron creaser quite warm over a gas or other light, crease the edges, and rub them with a rag until they are smooth. Trim the ends of the stops down thin.

Next prepare the billet, which is thirteen and one half inches long, by dampening it well and rubbing it down solid with a slicker ; cut out the end of the billet with a half round punch, and with a small edge tool take the edge off each side to one half the length, then stain, and rub smooth with a cloth. Mark off one and one half inches to go into the round of the rein, and five inches more for the stop ; crease up the billet and punch with a No. 6 round punch, dampen the end that enters the rein so that it will work easily, trim down to a feather edge, and then pound down to the mark, so that the stitcher can more easily pull the round up tight; this being done, tack the billet to the rein and it is ready to be stitched.

The billet, as has been stated, is marked off five inches, three inches of which are for the half-inch loops before and behind the buckle ; this part is channeled the width of the box loop, and a space of one half inch each way from this loop is stitched with seven or eight stitches, drawn tight; these make the rein firmer, and give it a better finish.

After the billet is stitched, the rein is ready for
filling up. To do this, first see that the filling is
thoroughly wet, so that it can be shaved down
evenly, and, when the rein is closed up, can be
pounded down to a true and smooth round. In
filling up, care should be taken not to dampen the
rein too much, for if too wet the leather can not be
trimmed off smoothly with a spokeshave, and
when dried out it becomes hard and brittle ; also,
when filling off, the channel, instead of being close
and smooth, will raise and become uneven. The
proper course is to dampen it with a sponge, and
pound down immediately. To do this, take a
large awl, run it through one of the holes in the
billet, fasten the rein to the board, and, with a
shoemaker's hammer, pound one edge down to
the end of the rein ; then turn the rein over, commence at the same point as before, and pound the
other side down ; in this way the rein is evenly
prepared to receive the filling. In placing the
latter in position, always put in the longest pieces
at the commencement, and use the short pieces
down at the neck of the rein. At the end, where
the handpart is sewed in, put in an end piece, or
sew the handpart into the round ; either will do,
but the former is the better plan. After the rein
is closed, if a little dry in places, dampen it slightly with a sponge, then trim off with a large-sized
edge tool, and also trim off the filling close to the
rein ; then pound down on a board iron made for
this purpose, having a half-round groove in which
to place the rein. The use of this groove mate-

rially lessens the labor and helps to secure a good round. Some workmen use a flat stone or board iron without a groove, but it is poor policy to do so, as it has a tendency to flatten the leather where it bears upon the stone.

The rein is now ready to be rounded up, which is done by pulling it through the rounding machine three or four times, after which trim off the edges with a sharp spokeshave as round and evenly as possible; dampen the rein slightly with a moist sponge, pull it through the rounding machine three or four times more, and then with a hand rounder rub up and down all over the round, the object being to touch all the parts that the machine has failed to reach, thereby making them smooth. Then, with a sponge and a solution of oxalic acid, clean off the rein and hang it up to dry. When dry, or nearly so, apply a small quantity of a stain made of annotta and saffron in the proportion of one pint of the former to a half gill of the latter. After dampening the reins, block up the loops, trim nicely from the end of the rein to the box loop, stain, and rub down smoothly; dampen the round slightly with the stain, and rub briskly until a nice, smooth polish appears. In order to preserve the color on the rein, dissolve shellac in alcohol, and with a clean sponge apply it to every part of the rein; this, in addition to preserving the color, produces a good lustre on the leather.

Rein ends can be made up in a variety of styles,

but the general directions for manufacture are the same. Their use is to prevent the Martingale ring coming in contact with the buckle, or bit ring, where it will catch fast, and at the same time provide a neat ornament for the end of the rein. In cutting the harness maker should aim to make them not less than one quarter of an inch wider than the inside diameter of the Martingale ring. Figs. 1, 2, 3, and 4 show four patterns, all but fig. 4 being made up as previously directed. This is made without buckles, but a small piece of steel is bent at the point where the rein joins to the ornament, which is stitched in between the straps. This steel hook is sometimes used with other styles of rein ends.

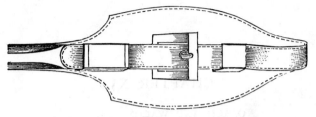

FIG. 1.

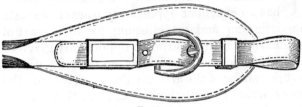

FIG. 2.

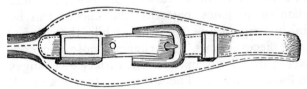

FIG. 3.

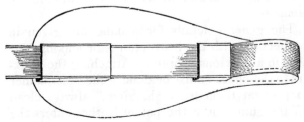

FIG. 4.

CHAPTER XVI.

COACH AND WAGON BRIDLES.

IN manufacturing bridles, the harness maker has an excellent opportunity to exercise taste in designing and embellishing, for in no part of the harness is there so much opportunity given to introduce new ideas without interfering with the proper shape of the article ; then, too, they are the most ornate part of the harness, and there is less liability to overdo in decoration. The winkers may be made in a variety of styles, stitched plain or in fancy patterns; the cheeks can be finished up in different ways, while the crowns, face pieces, fronts, gag runners, nose and chin pieces are all susceptible of a variety of changes in form or finish. There is no portion of a coach harness more difficult to make, and for that reason the bridle maker holds a high position in the business.

The general details for making are given in connection with the instructions for making harness in a previous chapter. Attaching the winkers to the cheeks must be done in the best manner to prevent them from " hinging;" always clean off the gum where the patent leather enters the

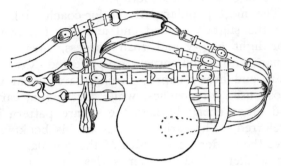

FIG. 1.

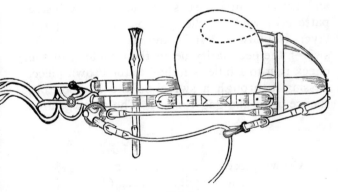

FIG. 2.

cheek pieces, so that the paste may adhere, and
skive off to secure a smooth job.

The most popular patterns for coach winkers
are the slightly ovaled end and the full oval.
For light buggy and road harness, square or
square with round corners are preferred. Coupé,
team, and heavy express winkers are similar to
those used for coaches, while for wagon, cart,
and other cheap harness the square pattern is
preferred. The various plates in this book will
give the reader a good idea of the popular form
for winkers, though other styles are also used
to a considerable extent. The illustrations of
bridles in connection with this chapter show
some of the distinctive patterns in detail. Fig. 1
represents the English coach bridle with the oval
winker. This is the popular style for all coach
and heavy coupé harness, though no exclusive
pattern of winkers, cheek loops, or crown piece
layers is followed. It is known as the bradoon
swivel, the peculiarity being the attaching of the
check rein to a billet stitched to the crown piece,
passing it through a swivel on the bradoon bit,
thence up to the gag runner. The cuttings are :

	Length, inches.	Width, inches.
Crown piece	28	$1\frac{3}{4}$
Ends, split	$6\frac{1}{2}$	$\frac{3}{4}$
Layer	9	$\frac{3}{4}$
Gag runners	12	$\frac{3}{4}$
Front	28	$1\frac{1}{8}$

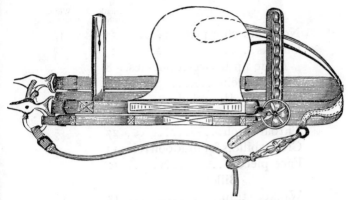

Fig. 3.

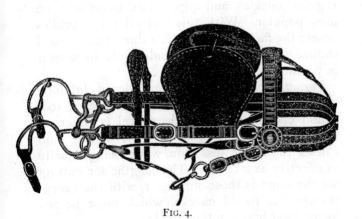

Fig. 4.

	Length. inches.	Width. inches.
Nose and chin piece	33	$1\frac{1}{8}$
Cheeks	29	$\frac{3}{4}$
Made up between buckles.	8	
Bradoon rein	26	1
Rounded	20	
Center rein	60	$\frac{3}{4}$
Throat latch	27	$\frac{3}{4}$
Crown billets for bradoon rein	13	$\frac{3}{4}$
Face piece	12	
Billet		$\frac{3}{4}$
Winker strap	13	$1\frac{1}{2}$
Billet	5	$\frac{3}{4}$
Split	7	

The narrow loops and center bar buckles give this bridle a showy appearance, but the regular buckles and pipe cheek loops are the most popular. With this and all other bridles where the face piece is used, a thin piece of steel should be attached to the under side to keep it in position.

Fig. 2 represents another style of bradoon bridle, in which the bradoon bit is attached to a round cheek piece, and the swivel is dispensed with. It is claimed that a bridle of this kind causes the horse less pain, while being equally as effective as a check. The lengths for cutting are the same as those for Fig. 1, with the exception of the round cheeks, which must be ten inches long between the buckles.

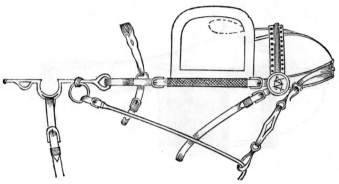

FIG. 5.

FIG. 6.

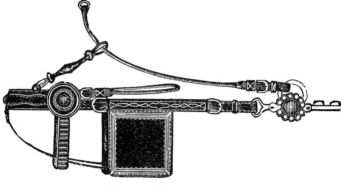

FIG. 7.

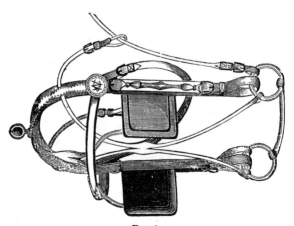

FIG. 8.

Fig. 3 represents a third style of bradoon bridle, the extra cheek being flat.

Fig. 4 is also a bradoon bridle, but differs from the preceding ones in the manner of attaching the gag runner.

Fig. 5 represents a plainer style of bridle, suited to the lighter grades of coach and road harness.

Fig. 6 is designed for light double harness; one of the plainest kinds in use.

Fig. 7 represents a very neat bridle for single or light double harness.

Fig. 8, a plain bridle with a half Kemble-Jackson check.

Fig. 9, a heavy bridle for a team harness; the tugs on the ends of the checks are cut of patent leather, and may be ornamented with monograms or initial letters.

Fig. 10 is designed for a team bridle; but is made up without winkers; the cheeks may be made as represented, or rounded. The latter appear much the lightest. The face piece may be flat or round. The most popular style of finishing is to round the ends below the face ornament, leaving the upper part flat.

Fig. 11 represents a plain team harness bridle without winkers, the cheeks made up with patent leather ornaments and without buckles; the crown, cheeks, and throat latch billets are cut of one piece; the ornaments are stitched to the cheeks at the front piece, and held in position by two loops; or the patent leather ornaments may

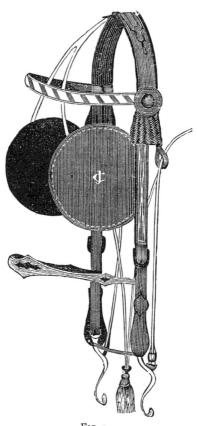

FIG. 9.

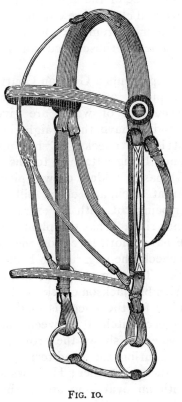

FIG. 10.

be lined and stitched, leaving the ends open to admit the cheek pieces; a cross face piece can be used in place of the nose piece, if preferred. The crown and cheeks are cut thirty-eight inches long. The measurements for the other straps are the same as those used for regular team bridles.

Fig. 12 represents a German Court bridle.

Crown pieces are made up in a variety of styles, a number of which are given on page 195. A and B have the straight layer, but different styles of cheeks; C has no layer, the gag runner being attached to the throat latch billet; D has a folded crown piece with the layer, throat latch, and cheek billets cut in one, the layer being cut with an extra billet for the gag runner ring; E has the plain double waved layer; F has a short layer for the half Kemble-Jackson check, the gag runner being attached to the check. The same style of layer is used for the full Kemble-Jackson check. In both instances the opening for the check is made by a wedge-shaped piece stitched between the layer and crown piece. G shows the crown, with a short layer for securing the head terret, and an extra billet for the gag runner; H shows a plain strap layer, with an oval loop and a ring for a gag runner. This is used for carrying the gag rein well up and close to the cheek. I shows the common fold crown, with a plain waved layer.

FIG. II.

FIG. 12.

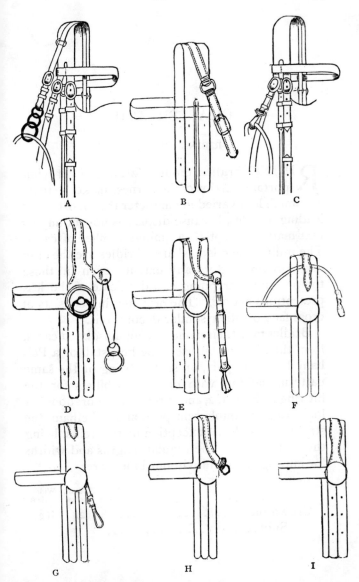

A

B

C

D

E

F

G

H

I

CHAPTER XVII

RIDING BRIDLES.

RIDING bridles, though forming a very important portion of the harness maker's stock, are much less varied in character than most other leading articles, because display is not an important matter except in a limited number of cases. The military and ladies' dress bridles are the only ones ornamented to any extent; even in these the principal strapping is a duplicate of the less pretentious article. The ornamenting consists of cross face or other similar decorations.

Bridles take their name, except in isolated cases, from the style of bit used, the headstall of a Pelham, bradoon, port, or snaffle being of the same pattern, made up with or without billets for the bit rings. Figs. 1, 2, and 3 represent a bradoon, or loose ring, a double rein port, and a Pelham, the strapping, with the exception of the reins, being the same in all. The regular lengths and widths for cutting with and without billets are:

	Length, inches.	Width, inches.
Crown piece	24	$1\frac{3}{8}$
Split	7	

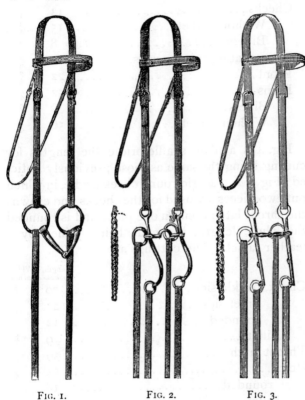

FIG. 1.   FIG. 2.   FIG. 3.

Bradoor.   Double Rein Post.   Pelham.

	Length, inches.	Width, inches.
Cheeks	13	¾
Without billets...............	15	¾
Billets.......................	8	¾
Throat latch, two buckles........	12	⅝
Front...........................	22	¾
Reins...........................	52	¾
Billets.......................	8	¾
Without billets...............	56	¾

Fig. 4 is a plain snaffle bridle, the lengths for cutting being the same as those previously noticed; Fig. 5 is a single round cheek bridle, in which but two pieces are used for the cheeks and crown; the throat latch is cut in one piece and is rounded the whole length, the ends being joined by a leather tassel. The cuttings are:

	Length, inches.	Width, inches.
Cheek, buckle side.................	20	¾
billet side....................	24	¾
rounded	12	
Billets.....	9	¾
Throat latch.......................	39	¾
Reins...........................	54	¾
rounded.......................	18	
Billets.......................✓....	9	¾
Front...........................	24	¾
rounded......................		11½
Curb straps....	22	½

Fig. 6 is a double cheek bridle with a plain port and a light bradoon bit. The cheeks and crown

FIG. 4.

Plain Snaffle.

FIG. 5.

Round Check.

piece for each bit are cut in one piece. The cuttings are :

	Length, inches,	Width, inches.
Port cheeks and crown..............	34	$\frac{3}{4}$
rounded..................	12	
Bradoon cheeks and crown.........	36	$\frac{3}{4}$
rounded..................	12	
Billets..	8	$\frac{3}{4}$

Fig. 7 represents another style of double cheek
bridle, the cuttings for which are the same as for
Fig. 5, both cheeks being of the same length;
the nose strap, which may be used or not, is cut
three quarters of an inch wide and twenty-eight
inches long, and rounded fifteen inches.

Fig. 8 represents a double cheek bridle, in which
the cheek pieces on each side are cut in one ; the
crown piece for the cheek is also cut as one ; it is
doubled and buckled on the crown, and is provided
with two small slide loops ; the throat latch and
crown are cut in one as are also the nose and chin
pieces. The cuttings are :

	Length, inches.	Width, inches.
Cheeks...........................	33	$\frac{3}{4}$
rounded..................	24	
Billets.......................	8	$\frac{3}{4}$
Crown piece, made up as hame strap	24	$\frac{3}{4}$
Throat latch......................	39	$\frac{5}{8}$

Fig. 9 represents a style of double cheek and
bit bridle made up with long cheeks and without billets. The cuttings are:

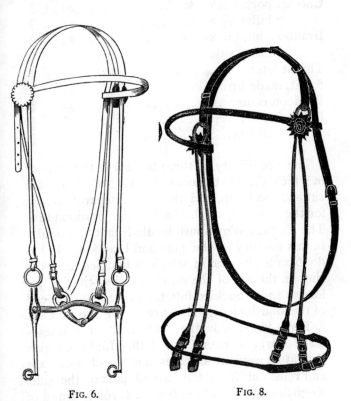

FIG. 6.

Double Check, Port, and Bradoor.

FIG. 8.

Double Check, Round.

	Length, inches.	Width, inches.
Cheeks, port, buckle side	20	¾
billet side	24	¾
Bradoon, bit, buckle side	22	⅝
billet side	26	⅝
Throat latch	22	⅝
Front, made up	13	½
Bradoon reins	90	¾
Port reins	96	¾
Billets	8	¾

The peculiarity of these bridles is the manner in which the port cheeks and throat latches are cut and made up, and the use of separate straps for the crown and cheeks for the bradoon bits. The English Weymouth bridle is not as popular in this country as the port and bradoon. It has double cheeks, one of which is buckled into the ring on the top of the bit check, the other is cut longer and is buckled into the rein ring at the end of the mouth piece, the bit used being the Pelham.

Three kinds of leather are used for bridles— black harness, russet, and buff. Light weights should be used in all cases, and the cheek straps and reins cut from the firmest part of the side. English russet has long been a favorite brand of leather, but the better grades of American are equal to it in every respect. Buff leather is used to a considerable extent for flat fancy bridles, to be used with saddles having seat and knee pads made of buckskin. This leather, being soft, is not

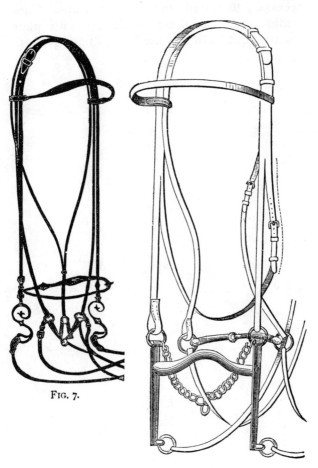

FIG. 7.

FIG. 9.

creased, and is stitched no more than is absolutely necessary to secure the various straps. Cheap bridles are sometimes made up with plated rosettes, but leather is used on all finer grades.

CHAPTER XVIII.

HALTERS.

HALTERS constitute a very important part of the harness maker's stock. The varieties are numerous; though apparently unnecessary, they are required to suit the preferences of different sections of the country, and render it obligatory on harness makers to be prepared at all times to meet the demands of their customers. The many illustrations in this chapter will enable the manufacturer to present to his customers correct representations to select from, while the lengths for cutting and the directions for making up will be found of great value in the work shop.

Fig. 1. represents the United States Government regulation halter, the principal merit of which is its strength and simplicity; it is easy to adjust, and can not be slipped off by the horse rubbing his head against posts or other objects. The lengths for cutting are:

	Inches.
Crown piece.....................	26
Chape	8
Cheeks..........................	14

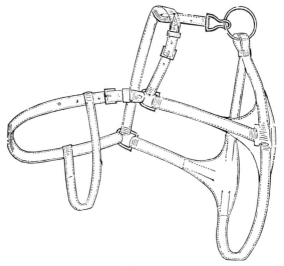

FIG. 2.

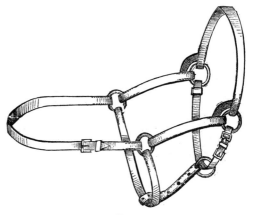

FIG. 1.

	Inches.
Throat piece	22
Chin piece, if double	30
single	18
Nose piece	18
Bolt piece	18
made up	6
Hitching strap, or stem	84
Billet	10

The regulation width is 1¼ inches; for general use, however, 1 inch is wide enough.

Fig. 2 is the Spanish halter; it bears a general resemblance to Fig. 1, from which it was modeled, but it is put together in a different manner; has a front and a cockeye attached to the bolt piece; all the straps but the front are cut long, and are doubled and stitched. The lengths for cutting are:

	Inches.
Crown piece	42
Buckle chape	8
Throat piece	28
Buckle chape	21
Cheek pieces	17
Nose piece	34
Chin piece	36
Bolt piece	10
Front	19

All the straps but the front are 1¼ inches wide; the latter is 1 inch wide; **D** rings are used for

FIG. 4.

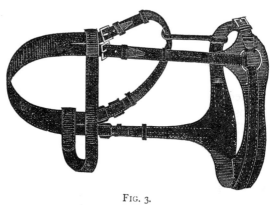

FIG. 3.

the upper, and square loops for the lower, ends
of the cheeks.

Fig. 3 is a heavy French stall halter of ornamental design and finish; it is used as a bridle
halter as well. The cutting lengths are:

	Inches.
Crown piece	24
End split	5
Cheek pieces	11
Nose piece	16
Chin piece	17
Chape	6
Throat latch	22
Front	18
Lining to nose piece	24

The crown piece is $2\frac{1}{4}$ inches wide, the cheeks
$1\frac{1}{4}$ inches, and all other straps 1 inch; the lining,
which is of patent leather, is $2\frac{1}{4}$ inches wide in
the center.

Fig. 4 is a heavy cleaning, or groom, halter. The nose piece is made with a flat iron
top, having three rings attached, these being
used to secure the horse's head in any desired
position. The nose piece plate is lined with
heavy leather, and padded. The lengths for cutting are:

	Inches.
Crown piece	22
Split	6
Cheeks	15

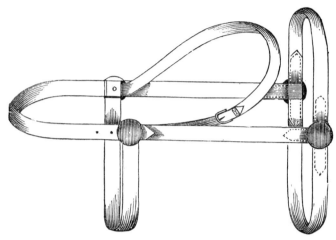

FIG. 6.

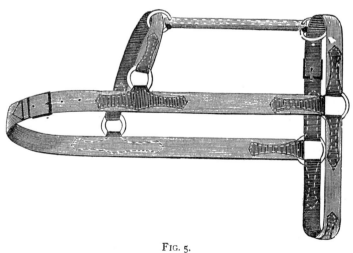

FIG. 5.

	Inches.
Throat latch.....................	22
Front..........................	27
Nose piece......................	13
Pad roll........................	11
Chin billet......................	11
Chape...................	6

The crown piece is cut 1½ inches, the throat latch ⅝ of an inch, all other straps 1 inch wide.

Fig. 5 represents a training halter of a neat and tasty design. All the principal straps are cut of bridle or buff leather, or of heavy twilled white web; the chapes of black harness leather for light-colored leather halters, and bridle or buff leather for web halters. The chapes are all of an ornamental pattern; those for securing the ends of the strapping to the rings are cut double, those holding the throat strap rings have a small billet by which the rings are secured. The lengths for cutting are:

	Inches
Long cheek piece................	23
Short " "	17
Throat piece.....................	18
Nose piece......................	12
Chin piece	10
Buckle chape.............	8
Bolt piece, made up.............	6½

The cheeks and bolt pieces are 1 inch wide, nose and chin pieces ⅞ of an inch wide.

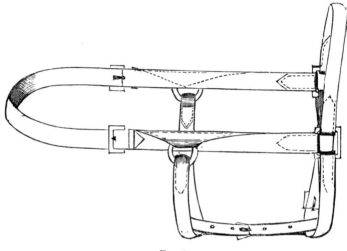

FIG. 8.

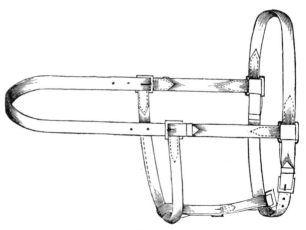

FIG. 7.

Fig. 6 is another style of training halter, which, like the preceding one, is made of buff, russet, or black leather, or of linen web. When the latter is used, the chapes should be of russet leather; metallic rosettes having a stout center pin and four loops on the under side are used to connect the various parts, thus dispensing with buckles except on the throat latch chape ; if these rosettes are not accessible, square loops may be used for the lower ends of the cheeks, and a buckle be attached to the short cheek piece, using fancy or plain leather for rosettes. The lengths for cutting are :

	Inches.
Long cheek, including crown piece	27
Short cheek	15
Front	19
Chin piece	18
Nose piece.........................	18
Throat latch.......................	17
Billet	9

If web and leather layers are used, deduct from these lengths 3 inches for each lap. The cheeks are cut $1\frac{1}{4}$ inches, the nose, front, and chin 1 inch, and the throat latch $\frac{7}{8}$ of an inch wide.

Fig. 7 represents a bitting halter, one of the most desirable styles in use. It closely resembles the straight cheek style of years past, the only difference being in the manner of attaching the throat piece, and in the use of two short cheeks. This may be made of buff, russet, or

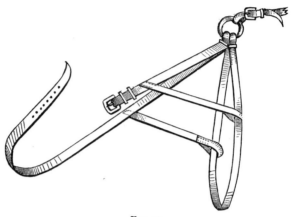

FIG. 10.

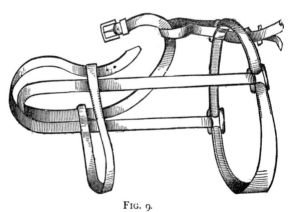

FIG. 9.

black leather. The buckles used on the checks are extra heavy, the side bar being made to answer as a substitute for loops to which the throat piece is attached. The lengths for cutting are:

	Inches.
Crown piece.....................	32
Cheeks...........................	10
Chin, double....................	24
Buckle chape...................	8
Nose...........................	18
Throat piece....................	22
Loop piece.....................	15

All the straps with the exception of the throat piece are cut 1¼ inches wide; this is cut 1 inch.

Fig. 8 closely resembles Fig. 7, the difference being in the manner of attaching the throat strap, and the use of but one buckle on the cheeks. The cuttings are the same, with the exception of the cheek pieces, which are cut:

	Inches.
Long cheek	25
Short cheek	16

The loops used for securing the throat piece are of metal or leather, and are provided with a short screw, by which they are held in position.

Fig. 9 represents a strong stable halter, of different construction than any previously noticed. The cheeks, crowns, and throat latch are cut so as to obviate the use of the usual buckles or rings in the cheek pieces. The billet to the stem

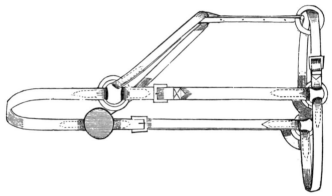

FIG. 12.

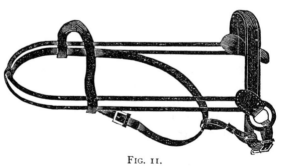

FIG. 11.

and the bolt, or loop piece, are also in one piece.
The lengths for cutting are:

Inches.

Long cheek, including throat latch .. 52
Short cheek, including billet to throat
latch 29
Front, double...................... 22
Nose, double...................... 23
Chin, double...................... 23
Billet to stem. 18

Fig. 10 represents another peculiar style, commonly known as the Yankee halter. It is designed for a slip halter, and is easily made. The lengths for cutting are:

Inches.

Head piece...................... 50
Nose piece...................... 28
Braces........................... 12
Hitching strap.................... 84

All the straps are cut of uniform width, either 1 or 1¼ inches. Attach the braces 9 inches from the ring on the head piece.

Fig. 11 represents a double cheek halter, designed to be used for training purposes. The lengths for cuttings are:

Inches.

Crown........................... 20
Buckle chape.................. 8
Cheeks........................... 22
Billets 9
Extra crown piece.............. 22

Inches.

Nose piece......................... 18

Chin piece, double.................. 24

Front.............................. 22

Throat latch....................... 22

The crown piece is cut 1 inch wide; all other straps, ¾ of an inch wide.

Fig. 12 represents another style of four ring halter, the buckles being in the cheek pieces; the rings may be covered with a rosette, if desired. The lengths for cutting are

Inches.

Crown............................. 17

Cheeks............................ 14

Cheek billets...................... 7

Nose piece......................... 18

Chin, double....................... 30

Throat piece....................... 26

Bolt piece......................... 5½

The cheeks, crown, and bolt piece are cut 1¼ inches wide; the other straps, 1 inch.

Fig. 13 is also designed for a training halter. The lengths for cutting are:

Inches.

Long cheek and crown 32

Short cheek....................... 15

Throat latch and crown in one...... 42

Nose piece, double................. 24

Chin piece, double................. 23

Loop piece........................ 8

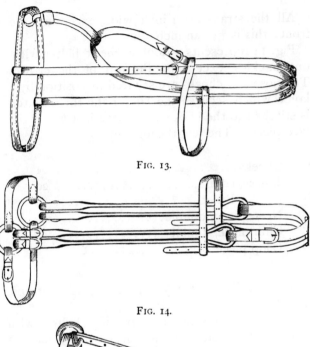

FIG. 13.

FIG. 14.

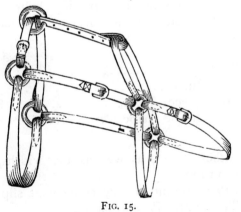

FIG. 15.

All the straps are 1 inch wide, excepting the front: this is ¾ of an inch.

Fig. 14 represents a double cheek halter without buckles, except on the top of the crown. The nose and cheeks are secured in position by a layer which secures the rings; the throat latch is stitched to the back cheek piece just below the face piece. The lengths for cutting are:

	Inches.
Cheeks	21
Throat latch	20
Billet	6
Nose piece, double	23
Chin piece, double	25
Loop piece	8

The cheeks are cut ½ inch wide; other straps, 1 inch.

Fig. 15 represents a four ring halter with front, and buckles on the cheeks. The lengths for cutting are:

	Inches.
Cheeks	12
Billets	5½
Crown piece	18
Buckle chape	8

All other straps, as well as the widths, the same as in Fig. 1

Fig. 16 represents a very convenient slip halter. The lengths for cutting are :

Inches.

Crown piece......................... 21
Throat and cheek pieces in one...... 38
Nose and chin piece in one.......... 24

All the straps are cut 1 inch wide.

Fig. 17 represents a convenient style of team halter to be worn with the bridle. The lengths for cutting are:

Inches.

Crown and throat latch in one....... 30
Nose and chin strap in one.......... 26
Cheeks............................. 10
Bolt piece......................... 7

Cuttings for a common bridle or three ring halter:

	Length, inches.	Width, inches.
Cheek, including crown piece.....	34	1
Short....................	12	1
Front...........................	24	1
Nose band.......................	18	1
Chin, doubled....................	30	$\frac{7}{8}$
Bolt piece......................	18	1
Throat latch....................	39	$\frac{3}{4}$
Stem............................	84	1
Billet....................	9	1
Bit strap......................	9	1

A web halter:

Crown...........................	24	$1\frac{1}{4}$
Cheeks..........................	8	$1\frac{1}{4}$
Chapes....................	5	$1\frac{1}{8}$

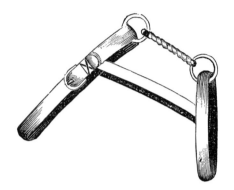

FIG. 17.

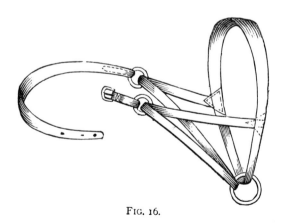

FIG. 16.

	Length, inches.	Width, inches.
Front	12	$1\frac{1}{4}$
Chapes	8	$1\frac{1}{8}$
Nose	13	$1\frac{1}{4}$
Throat latch, leather	39	$\frac{3}{4}$
Chin piece, leather	30	$\frac{3}{4}$
Bolt piece	18	1

Yankee one ring halter:

Crown piece, nose and chin in one	84	1
Braces	12	1

To make this halter, cut for the buckle tongue, and bend down the buckle lap; then measure off 12 inches, and bend down for ring; then 28 inches, and bend for nose band; then place the brace in the center between the front of the nose band and center of the chin piece at the ring; cross the strap through the ring, and bring the crown end up on the off side: this will place the buckle on the near side. Set the crown piece at an angle so as to take the upper end of the braces. This makes a convenient halter, which easily adjusts itself to the head of any horse.

CHAPTER XIX.

HORSE BOOTS.

THE artist who pictured a horse on the track with his legs encased in boots, etc., from the bottom of the hoof up to the body, was not so far from the truth as many persons would suppose, for there is no part of the limb, from the knee down, for which boots are not made. The illustrations in this chapter represent the general styles, though not all the varieties in the market. There are many patented boots, some of them possessing merit, a description of which would be of no practical use to the harness maker. There are several classes of boots, such as the knee, shin, ankle, quarter, and combination, each of which has its distinctive name.

The illustrations in this chapter have an advantage over those found elsewhere, in that nearly all are drawn in exact proportions; and the descriptions are such that a harness maker may readily furnish a customer with any desired pattern. Making horse boots is not a simple operation : success depends upon their being so constructed that they will retain their position without being strapped so tight as to interfere with the freest movement of the horse's leg. To accomplish this, the leather used for shields must be worked up firm and the securing straps placed where they will draw in direct lines. When fullness is to be given to the shields, the best plan is to cut out a V and stitch the edges together; they may, however, be stamped up with dies. For convenience, each class will be described separately.

Fig. 1 represents one of the best styles of knee boot in use; it is made of heavy bridle leather, cut in two pieces, as shown by A and B; the former is worked up nearly flat, except that portion below D, where it is shaped to fit to B, which is worked up full in the center; a gore is taken out at C, and the edges joined to secure the shape. The securing strap, D, is of medium weight bridle leather, and is stitched to the shield before the lining is put in. The lining, which is of buckskin, is turned in all around, so that the edge is placed between the two pieces, and stitched down all around; a very little wool or hair is placed between the two, and the center is secured by stitching at the highest point in the shield B. The securing strap is also lined with buckskin and stuffed with felt; the billet, which is twenty inches long and one half inch wide, is stitched to the securing strap. The buckle chape is stitched to a strong loop at the other end of the main strap; the two small loops hold the billet in position, it being passed around the boot before it is buckled; the drawing is one quarter size.

Fig. 2 is a plain, heavy knee boot. This is cut

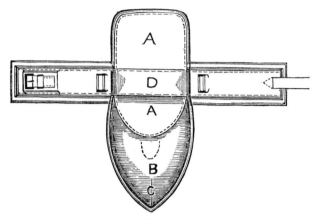

FIG. 1.

FIG. 2.

from one piece of leather ; that portion above the securing strap is flat, the lower part has a half inch raise in the center ; the lining is of buckskin, wool or hair being used for padding. The securing strap is cut of good, firm leather, and lined with buckskin, padded with felt. The billet is cut one half inch wide and fourteen inches long. There are five small loops, each one inch long, placed as shown on the main strap. The drawing is one quarter size.

Fig. 3 represents a peculiar shaped but desirable knee boot. It is cut from one piece of harness or bridle leather ; the cap piece is gored in two places, to produce the requisite fullness ; it is lined with buckskin and padded with a single thickness of felt ; the lining is cut large and the edge turned in so as to form a roll all around ; two heavy pads are attached to the under side as bearings ; one is shown by the line X, the other is placed directly under the buckle ; the center-pad is nearly one inch thick, the one under the buckle is about three quarters of an inch thick ; both are made of felt placed under the buckskin. This boot when made up is nine inches long. The proportions in the drawing are based upon that measurement.

Fig. 4 differs but little in shape from Fig. 3, but is made up plainer. The proportions are the same.

Figs. 6 and 7 represent two patterns of knee boots of an entirely different model from the above. They are also much lighter. The body of Fig.

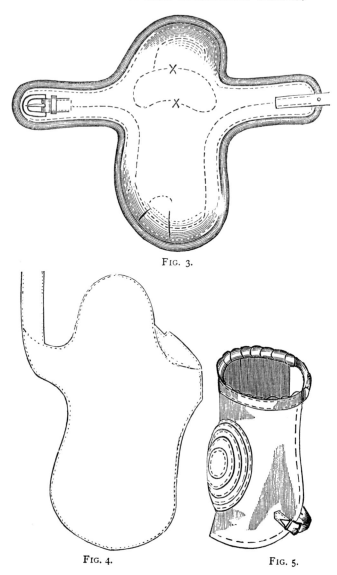

FIG. 3.

FIG. 4.

FIG. 5.

6 is made of enameled leather, lined throughout
with buckskin; the shield is of heavy harness
leather struck up full, and slightly padded with
felt. The bearing pads, shown by the dotted
lines, are raised about three quarters of an inch;
they are of felt, covered with buckskin. The
long or top billet is cut eight inches long and
three quarters of an inch wide; the bottom billet
is cut six inches long and three quarters of an inch
wide; a small gore is cut at X; the edges are
drawn together and blind stitched before the
lining is stitched in. The drawing is one third
the full size.

Fig. 7, though designed for the same purpose
as Fig. 6, is much lighter, and, being more open,
is less likely to bind when on the knee. The
lower billet is so placed that it does not bear
upon the cords sufficiently to displace it when the
knee is bent. It is made up in the same manner
and of similar material as Fig. 6. The upper or
leg strap is cut nineteen inches long and five
eighths of an inch wide; the lower billet is cut
ten inches long and one half inch wide. The
other proportions, as shown, are one third the
full size.

Fig. 5 represents a knee pad or breaking boot;
the body is made of heavy felt; the leg strap is
stitched to the felt and lined with buckskin;
the knee safe is made of several thicknesses of
bridle leather, worked up full in the center.

Combination boots are made in a great variety
of styles, there being at least fifty different pat-

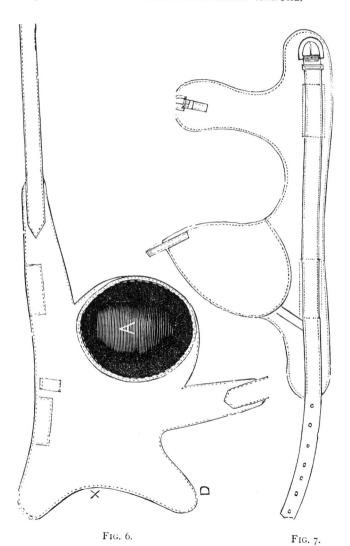

FIG. 6.

FIG. 7.

terns in use. The principal portion of the shield
is designed expressly to protect the shin ; to this
is attached a cap piece for covering the knee or
ankle. The styles illustrated comprise the regular lines, and, with the slight variations necessary
to secure a good fit, are all that are needed.

Fig. 8 represents a shin and ankle boot. The
body is made of heavy felt, the shield of harness
leather, worked up full at the ankle end ; the latter is stitched to the body with a single row
around the edge and a few stitches at each end.
The shaded spaces on each side represent strips
of leather ; the blank space A, strips of elastic
web ; these are attached to the body by the
stitching shown on the strips nearest the shield ;
the remaining portion of the webs and the straps
to which the buckle chapes and billets are attached are left loose, the portion of the body
under them acting as a safe ; by the use of these
elastic strips the boot is freed from the rigidity
so often noticeable, and the horse is relieved from
any undue pressure. The shield when made
up is eight inches long ; the reduced size of the
drawing is based upon that measurement.

Another style of shin and ankle boot is shown
by Fig. 9, which may also be used as a shin and
knee boot. The body is of heavy felt, bound on
the top and bottom edges with thin leather, and
lined throughout with buckskin ; the shield is
padded with hair. The dimensions of this boot
are : body, nine inches wide and six and one half
inches deep ; the billets are four inches, and the

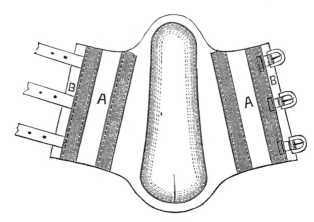

FIG. 8.

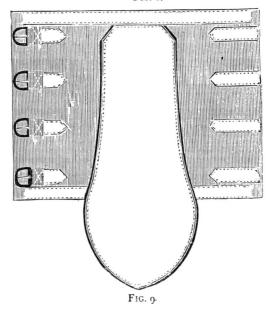

FIG. 9.

buckle chapes three inches, long. The shield is reduced in the same proportions as the body.

A light cord and knee boot is shown by Fig. 10. The body is made of black enameled leather, lined with buckskin, double stitched. The shield is of heavy harness leather, worked up full and padded with hair, the buckskin lining extending the full length of the shield. The billets are cut three eighths of an inch wide and seven inches long, the buckle chapes the same width and one and one quarter inches long; the proportions are one sixth the full size.

Fig. 11 illustrates a knee and cord boot of another pattern. The body is cut of medium weight harness leather, and bound with light enameled leather; the leg strap is made of strips of black enameled leather, stitched together on the edges and through the center, and stuffed with hair; it is attached to the body by two thicknesses of black enameled leather; the shield is of heavy leather, padded with hair. The billets on the body are five inches long and one half inch wide; the billet on the leg strap is five and one half inches long and one half inch wide. The drawing is one sixth actual size.

Fig. 12 represents a combined shin, ankle, and cord boot. The body, B, is of heavy felt, bound with buckskin; the shield, A, of heavy harness leather, worked up full at the lower end; D, a piece of heavy leather, lined with buckskin, stuffed with hair so as to make a cushion about one half inch thick; C, two pieces of elastic

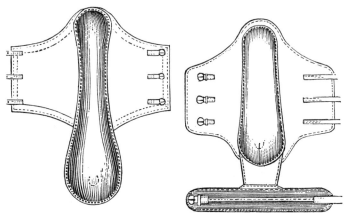

FIG. 10.   FIG. 11.

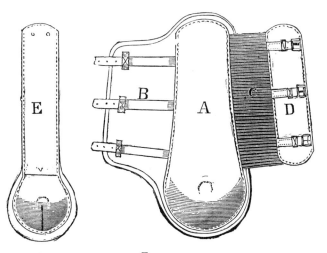

FIG. 12.

web, the outside piece being cut a little wider than the other; the web is secured in position by the stitching which is used to attach the shield A and piece D to the body and lining; the billets are attached at the shield, and pass through small loops near the outer edge of the body; E represents the cord piece, made of heavy leather, lined with buckskin at the lower end, an inside layer being attached at the top of the cap and extending up to the top, where there are two holes, as shown in E, through which a round leather lacer passes, and by which the top ends are joined. When the cord piece is used, the thin piece is placed between the two pieces of web, C, and the top, secured by the lacer. The drawing is one fourth the actual size.

Two other styles of combination boots are shown by Figs. 13 and 14, an ankle and wrist boot. Fig 13, the body, is of heavy blue kersey, bound with light enameled leather; the shield is of heavy harness leather; the ankle portion is worked up full and hard; owing to the thickness of the material used in the body, no stuffing is used. The wrist strap is of elastic web; it passes between the shield and body, and is held in position by the stitching. The billets for the top are cut five and one half inches long and one half inch wide; the kersey body is cut nine and one half inches wide across the top and eight inches long; the shield is three and three quarter inches in diameter; all other parts are drawn to the same scale.

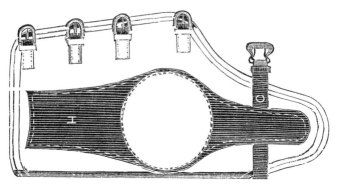

FIG. 14.

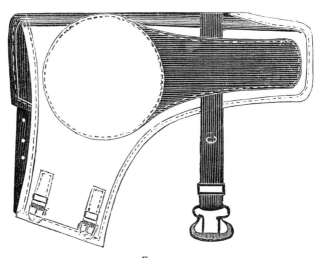

FIG. 13.

Fig. 14 represents a combined shin, ankle, and wrist boot, made up of the same materials and in the same manner as Fig. 13. It is cut two inches longer than the latter, otherwise the proportions are the same; the billets are cut five inches long and one half inch wide. The wrist web is seven-eighths of an inch wide.

Fig. 15 shows a design of shin and ankle boot intended as a protection to the hind legs. The body is made of black enameled leather, lined throughout with buckskin. The shin shield has but little fullness, and is padded on the under side with hair placed between the enameled leather and the buckskin, the padded section being quilted to hold the hair in position. The body to the ankle portion is also of enameled leather, lined in like manner as the shin body; the shield is of harness leather, worked up full and hard. The set of this piece depends much upon the position of the billets and buckle chape; these are shown in their proper position. The body of the shin boot is eight and three quarter inches across the top and ten and three quarter inches across the bottom; the shield is seven and three quarter inches long; the ankle shield is two and three quarter inches in diameter, all other proportions being relatively the same. The ankle billet is cut eight inches long and five eighth inches wide, about one half the length being rounded and covered with buckskin.

A shin, ankle, and speedy cut boot is shown by

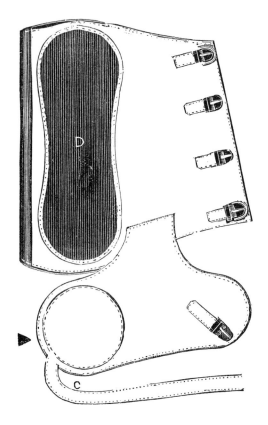

FIG. 15.

Fig. 16, which, like the preceding boot, is designed for the hind leg, the pattern being one of the best in use; the speedy cut portion, C, is made up separate from the shin boot, and is held in position by the lower billet of the latter passing through a long loop on the top end. The body, B, is of heavy kersey; the shield, of harness leather, worked up slightly in the leg part and full at the ankle; the under side of the shield is padded with hair; the pastern piece, C, is of black enameled leather, lined with buckskin; the shield, D, of harness leather, slightly rounded up; the billet attached to the pastern piece is covered for about one half its length with buckskin. The two upper boot billets are five inches long and five-eighths of an inch wide; the lower billet is cut nine inches long; the pastern billet is cut eight inches long, one half inch wide. The illustration is drawn to one quarter the full size.

Fig. 17 represents an improved ankle boot, lighter than most other kinds, and the location of the shield is such as to give greater protection to the ankle than that of the ordinary boot. The body is cut of harness leather; the shield, which is two and one half inches in diameter, is made of harness leather, worked up full and hard; a gore is taken out of the body, the edges are closed up smooth under the concave of the shield. Two bearing cushions are used, one under the buckle chape, the other as shown by the dotted lines near the billet; these are of felt, covered with buckskin; the one under the chape is two and

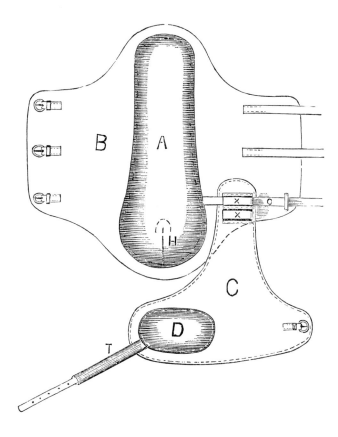

Fig. 16.

one quarter inches; the other, one and one half inches long and seven eighths of an inch wide; the boot is lined throughout with thin patent leather. The full measurements are: length on the top line, eight and one half inches; width of square ends, one inch; depth at the widest point, four inches. The center of the shield is six and one quarter inches from the top corner at the billet end and five inches at the buckle end; the billet is six inches long and one half inch wide.

Fig. 18 represents a plain, cheap ankle boot; the body is of heavy kersey, single or double; the shield is of harness leather, worked up full and hard at the ankle; the shield is six inches long and three and one half inches wide at the widest point and two inches wide at the top; the proportions of the body are based upon this measurement. The billets are five and one half inches long and one half inch wide; they, as well as the buckle chapes, are stitched to the body two and one half inches back of the edges.

A more expensive boot is shown by Fig. 19. The shield is of heavy russet leather struck up full and hard; the body is of heavy kersey, bound with buckskin; the leg strap is of russet leather; it is nine inches long and one inch wide it, as well as the shield, is secured to the body by a single row of stitching. The various proportions are: shield, four and one half inches long, three and one half inches wide at the

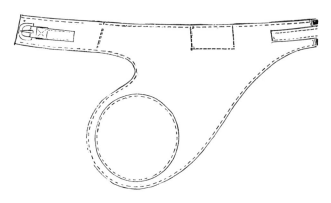

FIG. 17.

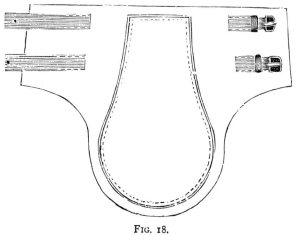

FIG. 18.

broadest point and two inches at the leg strap; the bearing pad, A, is one and one half inches long and one half inch thick; the billet is cut six inches long and one half inch wide.

Fig. 20 represents the hard leather cup ankle boot. The body is cut of heavy harness leather; a large gore is cut out of the top side, the edges of which are afterwards joined and blind stitched on the outside; the edges of the gore must be cut with a slight curve, in order to secure a regular circular fullness; the layer is cut of heavy leather, worked up full and stitched to the body; the buckle chape is cut three and one half inches long, and the billet eleven inches long. Two bearing cushions are used; one is shown by C, the outlines of the other by the dotted line near the top of the shield. These are of buckskin, stuffed with hair. The inside of the boot is skived off smooth all around the lower edge, care being taken to avoid all irregularities. The small cut A represents a side view of this boot. The large drawing is one half actual size.

Heel boots constitute a distinct class, of which there is a great variety; but those shown by the illustrations are all that are required for general use. Fig. 21 represents a well fitting boot of this class; the body is cut of medium weight harness leather; the layer is cut of heavy stock, worked up hard and stiffened by the layer under the shield; three gores are cut out of the top of the body, and the edges are joined and secured by blind stitches; a small section is gashed to form

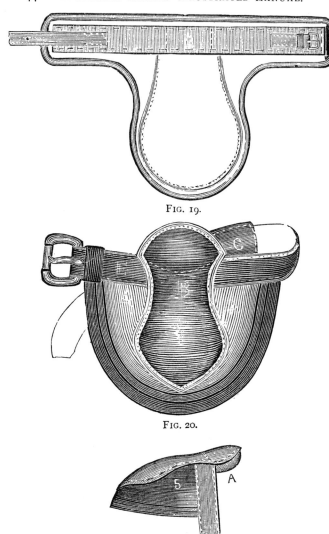

Fig. 19.

Fig. 20.

a fringe. The body is cut nine and one half
inches long on the top line, four and one half
inches deep in the center, and three inches at
the ends ; the shield is six inches long and two
and one half inches deep ; the billets are three
inches long and one and one half inches wide.

A plain, serviceable quarter boot is shown by
Fig. 22 ; it is made of a single piece of heavy harness leather, lined with felt ; the top edge is cut
as shown to provide a yielding surface and prevent injury to the horse ; six gores are taken
out of the bottom ; the edges are joined to produce the required shape ; the felt lining extends
to the top and within one half inch of the bottom,
and is secured as shown by the lines of stitching.
Buckles are not used, the ends being fastened by
means of loops attached to one, and holes cut
through the other to admit their passing through ;
they are then locked by a heavy billet as shown.
An ordinary boot is fourteen inches long on the
top line of stitches, the line being described by a
twelve inch radius ; the lower line is contracted
by the goring to twenty inches ; the depth when
made up is four inches.

Fig. 23 represents a toe boot for the hind foot ;
this is made up of heavy harness leather ; the top
section, indicated by the dotted line, is lined with
buckskin and padded. The full length of the
body is twelve inches ; depth, five and one half
inches ; the bottom line has a sweep of three
inches ; the buckle and roller loop chape is cut
three and one half inches long.

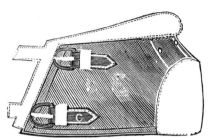

FIG. 21.

FIG. 22.

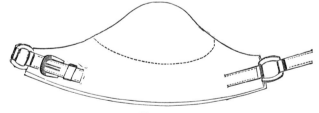

FIG. 23.

FIG. 24.

Another boot designed for the same purpose is shown by Fig. 24; this is cut of heavy leather, the top being lined with buckskin to make a cushion one inch deep.

Toe weight boots are designed for an entirely different purpose than those previously noticed, but they properly belong to this department.

Fig. 25 represents a boot with two weights, A; these are of lead, covered with leather. The body of the boot is of heavy leather, cut twenty-one and three quarter inches long on the lower line, and three and one eighth inches deep in the center. The billet is fourteen inches long and five eighths of an inch wide; the buckle chape is nine and one half inches long; it is attached to the lower edge of the body, and passes through a slot on the opposite side; the billet is attached in like manner and passed through a similar slot.

Another toe weight is shown by Figs. 26 and 27; the body, A, is of leather, having two slots as shown by X; the weight, B, is of lead, secured by an adjustable hook shown by Fig. 27; this is secured by a single strap which passes through the slots in the body and hook. A combined weight and quarter boot is shown by Fig. 28. The body is cut of one piece, of heavy leather, the quarter form being produced by gores; the quarter is lined with heavy felt and stiffened by layers; the toe weight and securing hook are secured by a piece of leather stitched to the body; the securing strap is stitched to the toe, and passes through a roller loop back to the buckle.

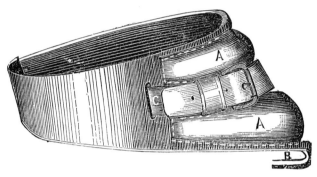

FIG. 25.

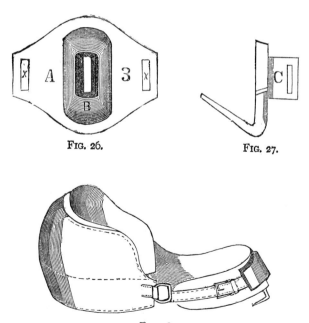

FIG. 26.

FIG. 27.

FIG. 28.

CHAPTER XX.

IN describing harness mountings, it is not the intention of the author to draw comparisons as to the respective merits of any class or style. The sole aim is to give a correct description of the various kinds, their peculiarities of manufacture, and such other information as will enable the reader to judge as to the adaptability of any particular style for a specific use.

In order that they may be fully explained, they will be divided into five classes, as follows: Plated, whether silver, gold, or nickel; pure metal; covered, whether leather or composition; japanned, and tinned.

Plated mountings are divided into two classes —close plate, those in which the fine metal is rolled out in thin sheets and applied as a covering to the iron or composition forming the body of the article, and caused to adhere by means of solder and heat; electro plate, those in which the fine metal is dissolved and formed into a liquid solution, into which the articles to be coated are suspended, and by the application of an electric current the fine metal is evenly deposited upon the surface of the iron or composition.

The silver used for close plating is rolled out in sheets of various thicknesses, and designated by numbers, the lightest being No. 1 ; following this are three grades, designated as No. 1½ light, fair, and stout, the former weighing three penny-weights to a foot in length by 6½ inches in width ; the second weighs 3½ pennyweights, while the third weighs 4½ pennyweights. Next to these are three grades, designated as No. 2 light, fair, and stout. The first weighs 5½, the second 6½, and the third 7½ pennyweights to the foot. Following these are three grades, designated as No. 2½ light, fair, and stout. The first weighs 8½, the second 9½, and the third 10½ pennyweights to the foot. The second is also designated as "Knob;" and the third, "Heavy Knob." The latter is seldom used on harness mountings, as it can not be worked to an advantage except by the hard solder process, which is too expensive for harness work. "Knob" silver is the heaviest used for the regular trade.

It will be seen that there are eight grades of silver below the "Knob," which explains in part why there is so great a difference in the prices of plated goods of any one pattern ; for, based upon the government standard, a foot of No. 1 silver, 6½ inches wide, would be worth 13.6 cents, while a foot of "Knob" silver would be 64.6; but the actual difference in the prices of the rolled plate is even greater than this. Then, too, the cost of labor is much greater for putting on heavy than light silver. The former is so thin that but little labor is required to solder it to the article to be plated, while the extra thickness of the latter necessitates extra skill and time.

Buyers who are not experts are at a loss how to determine the quality of the plate. This can be done by examining the surface closely ; the thinner the silver the less dense and perfect the surface. No. 1 will show minute holes in great number, while the surface of " Knob" will be perfect to the naked eye. It is not so easy to distinguish between two succeeding grades, but by a little care a person who handles these goods can learn to select each distinct grade. Close plate can be easily distinguished from the electro plate. All that is required is to breathe upon the polished surface, and if it is close plate the seam where the metal is joined will be seen at a glance, it showing a bluish streak ; the heavier the plate the more distinct the seam.

Electro plate is less durable than close plate ; but when deposited in sufficient quantity and hand burnished, it will wear well ; the surface, however, is less perfect than the former, as the thin coating of silver is deposited evenly over the entire surface, and an irregularity in the casting will show itself after the work is burnished ; in fact, blemishes are more easily detected after being plated and burnished than before, as the minute depressions can not be reached by the burnisher, and they therefore show dead, white spots.

The peculiar white lustre of silver distinguishes

it from other metals, but there are other tests by which the uninitiated may satisfy themselves as to the quality. The simplest is to prepare a cold saturated solution of bichromate of potassa in nitric acid. A little of this may be applied to the surface (which must be perfectly clean) by means of a glass rod, and washed off immediately with cold water. If the article tested is pure silver, a blood-red colored mark will appear ; if the article is German silver, the liquid appears brown, but the mark shows no shade of red. On other white metals there are various actions, but in none but the silver does the red mark appear.

Persons unacquainted with the nature of silver condemn an article as impure because of its tarnishing. This is erroneous, as pure silver assumes a dingy reddish brown, and loses its lustre more readily than some of the composition white metals.

Gold plating is always done by the electro process, the other processes for applying it to coarser metal not being adapted to harness mountings. It is the most showy but frailest plating in use ; the thin deposit is naturally soft, and but little friction is required to remove it. If hand burnished, the gold is made more dense than otherwise ; but even this is not as durable as other plating. There is no such an article of manufacture as close plate gold, nor can there be unless a solder can be produced which will melt under a lower heat than gold, and as there is no such sol-

der at this time, all claims of a gold covered article being close plate are fraudulent.

The introduction of nickel as a covering for
mountings has produced a marked change in
some lines of goods, supplanting as it has in a
great measure burnishing on bits, stirrups, spurs,
etc., and being largely used as a plate for all kinds
of harness mountings. The nickel is deposited by
the electro process, but, as it is a hard metal, it
wears well. The color is a bluish white, more
closely resembling finely polished steel than any
thing else. It does not tarnish easily, and will
not rust. The only objection to it aside from
the color is that it will sometimes peel—that is,
the nickel will become detached from the iron or
composition core; but this is due either to some
defect in cleaning the surface to be plated or in
the manner of depositing the nickel. Improvements are being made in the process of depositing the nickel, and there is every reason to believe
that the objectionable features will be overcome,
and with the reduction in price it will take the
place of tinned and other low priced white metal
goods.

The next class are those goods made of some
composition metal, such as brass, oroide, aluminum, and German silver. Brass has long been a
favorite mounting, though in this country it has
been deemed better suited to express and other
heavy mountings than for coach or light carriage
harness; but fashion has once more brought it

into use on coach harness, and it is likely, for a time at least, to assume the position held by gold for some years past. The advantages of brass are that it can be cast to any form, retains its malleability, is quite dense, and readily receives a brilliant polish; but its proneness to tarnish is an objection which tends to overcome its good qualities. The color is regulated by the proportions of the metals forming the compound, and skill in the moulder in turning it off just when it has been raised to the proper heat.

Oroide, like brass, is a yellow metal, and when first introduced was recommended as a substitute for gold; when polished it has a golden color, but it tarnishes too easily to be used without being plated. It, however, furnishes an excellent base for gilding, and for that reason is largely used. It can be cast as easily as brass, and is equally malleable; it can also be used for plating iron articles which are to be gilded, but if not plated or gilded it possesses but few advantages over ordinary brass.

Aluminum, or, as it is also called, alumina bronze, is the finest yellow metal produced; its color closely resembles that of gold, while it is susceptible of as high a polish as the latter; it is tough, though next to gold in lightness, but its high price prevents its being used for any but the most expensive mountings.

German silver is used to a considerable extent for mountings which are to be plated with silver. For this purpose it is the best white metal known ; other kinds have been introduced, but they have not proven suitable for mountings. The objection to all composition castings is their lack of rigidity, and they should never be used for check rein hooks of any kind ; these should be of iron, and plated to correspond with the terrets, etc.

Composition possesses one great advantage over iron which should be understood by harness makers and consumers. It does not rust, and can therefore be used in localities where iron can not, owing to the proneness of the latter to rust—particularly on the sea coast, where the sea air acts very injuriously on plated mountings.

Covered mountings consist of two kinds, those in which the metal is covered with leather, and, secondly, those having a metal core covered with a plastic composition. Leather covered is one of the oldest styles of mounting in use, but it was many years before it reached the state of perfection so noticeable at the present time. The durability, as well as the appearance of these mountings, depends upon the character of the leather used and the manner of putting it on. Calfskin, or very fine grained kip, are the only kinds of leather suited to covering mountings, but many of the cheaper grades are covered with sheepskin or thin split leather. Those conversant with working leather can readily understand the advantage arising from the use of thin, light stock, the work of putting on being reduced at least one half thereby. The inferior character of the work shows itself in a short time in the seams ripping or the leather cracking. Thick, firm leather requires more care in putting on and stitching, but it finishes much finer, and is more durable than the cheaper work.

The manner of covering is very simple : the leather is first cut to the required shape ; it is then soaked in water until it is soft and pliable, after which paste is applied, and the leather is worked around the metal by means of slicking sticks, and the edges joined by means of pinchers, or by plac-ing the article in dies and pressing them together and allowing them to remain on until the leather is dry, after which the seam is stitched by hand or machine, the welt trued off, and the leather blacked and finished.

The liability of the seam ripping has caused manufacturers to resort to different methods of putting on the leather and securing it; one method is the use of two seams on the edges in place of the one center seam so long in use ; the advantage claimed for this method is the protec-tion given to one side of the seam by the metal lining, and at the same time the article produced is more ornamental.

Another plan is to dispense with the seam entirely on the outside ; this is done by joining the edges of the leather on the inside of the ring, these being protected by the lining; imitations of the double and single seams are produced by casting them on the iron and working the leather down smooth to the outlines of the metal. The most recent improvement in making leather covered mountings is to draw the leather over the metal ring, which has previously been channeled, to allow for the full thickness of the leather, the rim on the edge forming a perfect protection to the leather ; this style is known as the " Centennial," an illustration of which will be found on page 263. Small leather covered harness buckles are more generally used than any others, the greater portion of these being imported from England, where they are produced at much lower prices than in America.

The composition covered mountings are hard rubber and celluloid. The first was patented in 1866, by Ralph Dunham, of Connecticut, as a covering for harness buckles and rings ; in 1867 Andrew Albright, of Newark, N. J., obtained a patent for covering harness and carriage mountings with rubber, these two patents being the first taken out—though early in the history of hard rubber, experiments were made in covering harness mountings, but the idea was abandoned ; but since the two patents above mentioned were taken out great improvements have been made, and rubber mountings are an acknowledged success.

The manufacture of these mountings, though not directly connected with the manufacture of harness, is interesting, and a description of the process will serve to give the reader a general idea of their peculiarities and merits. Every article is made with a metal core of about the same weight as that used for leather covered work. This core, or casting, is first cleaned up and made perfectly true by being struck up in a die; if any portion is to be plated, this is done, and the article is then taken to the rubber room to be covered. The rubber used is of the best Para gum, mixed in the proportion of two parts of gum to one part of pulverized sulphur; it is furnished in long sheets, varying from one to four lines French measure in thickness, and is kept rolled up in enameled cloth. Sheets of the rubber are laid out on a table and cut to such shapes as are needed for each article to be covered. The various pieces are then laid out on a piece of enameled cloth and saturated with benzine, covered up, and allowed to remain in this condition overnight, by which time the rubber becomes sticky; it is then wrapped around the metal body, care being taken to exclude air and to firmly weld the edges; after covering, the plated parts, if there be any, are covered with tin foil, when they are ready to be vulcanized; to do this the goods are either placed in moulds, buried in soapstone, or hung in an open pan. The vulcanator is a large tube made of boiler iron, and sufficiently strong to sustain a very heavy pressure of steam. After the goods are in the vulcanator, the door is closed and packed tight and the steam let on; if the goods are in pans and are to be cured by “ open steam,” they are subjected to a heat of 20 degrees for one hour; 10 additional degrees are gradually added each hour, until 65 degrees are reached (where the goods are in soapstone, the heat is raised to 65 degrees at the start). After having been subjected to this heat for the proper length of time, the goods are removed, and all small articles, such as buckles, rings, etc., are thrown into a tumbling barrel and tumbled with charcoal and water until the rough edges are removed; they are then placed into a steam box and heated; each article is then placed into steel dies and pressed by powerful hydraulic presses; this sets the rubber, forms a true finish, and sets a row of imitation stitches; the smaller articles are again tumbled for a short time, when they are ready to be finished. Large articles have to be trued up by hand, then cleaned on the ash wheel, from which they are taken to the buff wheels; the first is used with rotten stone, the second is dry; having passed through these, the articles have a fine polish and a jet black color, after which they are lined and plated, and made ready for the market. Up to the present time these goods have never been made anywhere but in this country. They have a fine finish and are very durable, and will, without doubt, eventually become popular wherever harness is used.

Celluloid mountings are of recent origin, and are made only in this country. The composition is a chemical compound which closely resembles amber; it can be colored any desirable shade, and does not fade through use. These mountings, like those of rubber, have a metal core coated with the composition. The process of manufacture is interesting. The castings are first trued up; they are then taken to the stuffer to be coated; they are then placed into moulds, or " stuffing dies." These are made of metal. The recess for the casting is provided with a number of small iron pins, upon which the castings rest. The arrangement of the moulds is precisely the same as that for casting metal. After the castings are placed into position, the moulds are closed up and placed into a recess at the foot of the stuffing cylinder. The latter is nearly filled with celluloid, and heated up to 190 degrees. After the die is secured in its place, a plunger, which is worked by hydraulic pressure, descends upon the hot gum and forces it into the dies in sufficient quantities to completely fill the moulds and cover the metal cores. The die is then removed, and in a few minutes emptied of its contents, and again made ready for stuffing. After being stuffed, the goods are removed to a drying room heated by steam, and allowed to season. They are then taken to the hydraulic forming presses ; the mountings are put into highly polished steel dies, and submitted to a fifty-ton pressure, which renders the material compact and produces a finely finished surface, after which they are lined, plated, and finished up ready for delivery.

Black is the predominating color, but a very handsome imitation of russet, as well as a good flesh color, has also been produced. As there is no difficulty in securing any color, the production of other shades than those mentioned depends upon the demand.

Celluloid martingale rings are a new article of manufacture. These closely resemble ivory in appearance, are much stronger, and are sold at lower prices than the latter. They are made of solid gum, which, after being colored, runs out into tubes of the required size. These are cut up into rings and thoroughly seasoned, after which they are taken to automatic lathes and turned up. They are then polished, and packed ready for shipping.

Tinned mountings, or, as they are known by the trade, " XC plate," are among the cheapest lines of goods. The metal castings are thoroughly cleaned, and then dipped into molten tin. The quality of the deposit depends entirely upon the skill and care of the workman.

Japanned mountings are those covered with a coat of black varnish which is solidified by heat. These are plain, and, if properly made, quite durable. They are, however, so well known that no extended description is necessary.

The various illustrations of mountings in this chapter represent the popular styles now in the market, some of which are made by the general trade, while others are patented either as designs or as new articles of manufacture. The " Grant," " Bismarck," and " Arlington " are patented as designs ; the " Double Seam," as a design and a new article of manufacture. This was fully described in connection with other leather covered mountings. The "Imperial" is patented as a design. This is made of composition metal, either white or yellow, and lined with hard rubber, the latter being turned up and finished off flush with the outside, leaving a narrow black edge with a metallic band center. This pattern is not lined, the wear coming direct upon the rubber, which, owing to its hardness, will wear longer than metal linings. One pattern of the ball wire mounting is also patented. The wire of this is covered with rubber and finished perfectly plain, while the ball and base are plated.

The "Centennial" is another patented mounting. This is made of metal cast with a recess upon the outside of the band, into which leather is worked while wet; the ends, firmly secured at the post, are an imitation seam pricked in on both edges. The appearance of this is exactly the reverse of the "Imperial." The centre is black, and the lining, edges, and head are of metal.

The illustrations of post, pad, and bolt hooks and head terrets give a general idea of these articles, though not representing all the styles. All the popular patterns of terrets have hooks and fly terrets to match ; and in ordering, the harness maker or dealer can always procure them in sets or by the package.

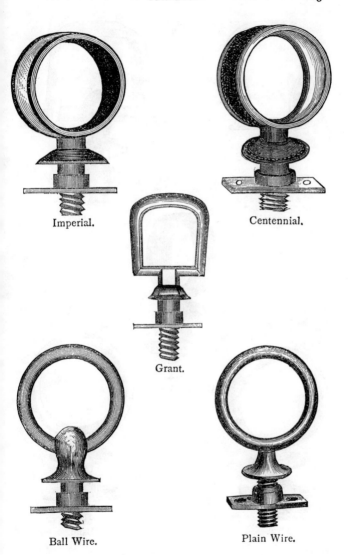

Imperial.

Centennial.

Grant.

Ball Wire.

Plain Wire.

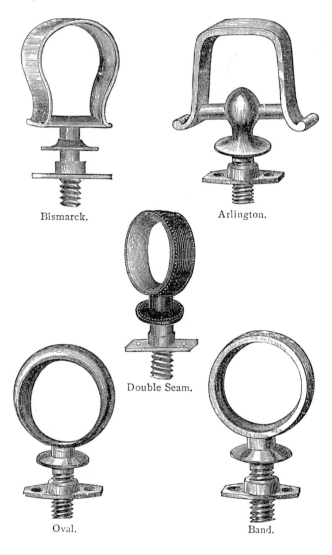

Bismarck.

Arlington.

Double Seam.

Oval.

Band.

Band.

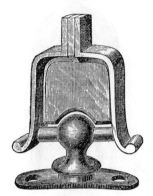

Arlington.

Oval.

Ball Wire.

Centennial.

Grant.

Wire Ball.

Acorn.

Band Fly Hook.

Oval Fly Hook.

Wire Ball.

Plain Wire.

Ball Wire, Fly.

Oval Post Hook.

Band C Hook.

Oval C Hook.

Oval Fly Bolt Hook.

Band Post Hook.

Wire.

Oval Pad Hook.

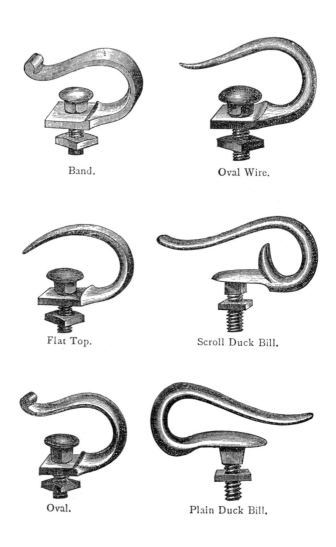

Band.   Oval Wire.

Flat Top.   Scroll Duck Bill.

Oval.   Plain Duck Bill.

CHAPTER XXI.

BUCKLES.

THE great variety of harness buckles in the market enables the harness manufacturer to procure those suited to every pattern of mounting. The illustrations in this chapter represent patterns suited to general use. In addition to these, buckles are made to match every style of mounting. An extended description is not necessary. The "Sensible" is one of the best in the market, owing to the form of the under side. It does not bend the strap as much as other patterns; it can be used with oval, "Grant," and band mountings. The "Victoria" and "Vermont" match well with the same patterns of mountings. The band, "Bonner," and "Square Philadelphia" are used with flat band patterns, the "West End" and other wire buckles with wire and oval terrets. Trace and collar buckles are made in as great variety as the smaller harness, the patterns being similar, but the center bar is used but little except as a trace buckle.

A buckle peculiar to this country—one in which the trace lies perfectly flat and is easily adjusted —is known as the "wedge tongue." This was the invention of Mr. Coles. Improvements were made by various persons, until at the present

time there are several varieties operating much
the same as, and bearing a close resemblance to,
the original. The " Coles," Fig. 1, represents the
original after having been so modified as to make
it practical. The " Coles," Fig. 2, represents
the latest improvement in the way of a spring,
which prevents the wedge getting out of place
when the trace is not drawn up tight. The
peculiarity of this buckle is in the wedge.
This is provided with a tongue or spur on the
under side, which sets into a hole in the trace and
takes the place of the ordinary tongue ; when the
trace is drawn up, the wedge bears against the
cross bar and holds the spur in position, and at
the same time produces a pressure which relieves
the strap at the hole of much of the strain which
would otherwise be put upon it.

Fig. 3 shows the " Kinne." This, when in position, bears a close resemblance to the " Cole,"
but it operates somewhat differently. The cross
bar is loose and the bearings upon the pier plate
press against it, producing the same result as the
wedge.

Fig. 4 represents the " Kinne" without loops.
This is used on single harness. These buckles
are very strong, and are made in all sizes from 1¼
to 2 inches

Fig. 1.

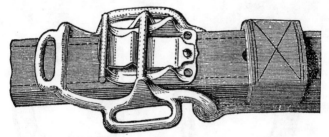

Fig. 2.

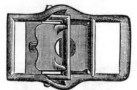

Fig. 3.

Fig. 4.

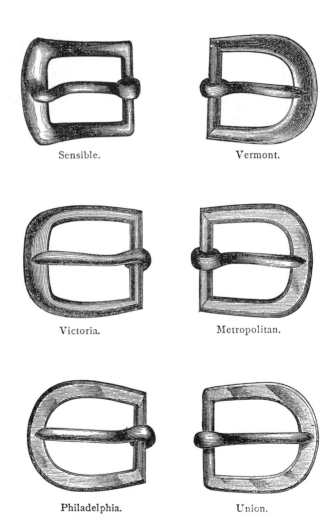

Sensible.   Vermont.

Victoria.   Metropolitan.

Philadelphia.   Union.

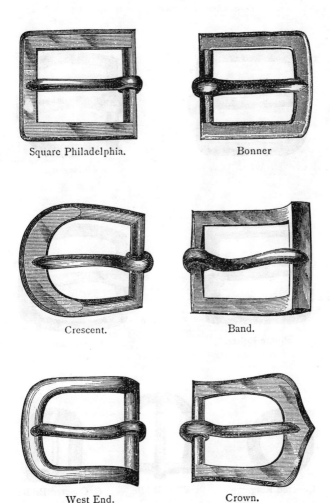

Square Philadelphia.

Bonner

Crescent.

Band.

West End.

Crown.

Wire.

Horseshoe.

Square Roller.

Barrel Roller.

Covered Ring.

Wire Bridle.

Covered Bridle.

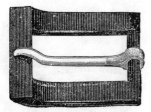

Ribbon.

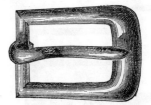

Sensible.

Light Band.

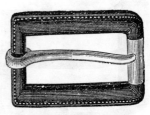

Covered Roller.

Band.

Covered.

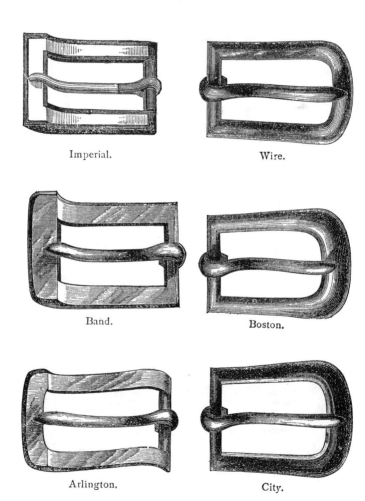

Imperial.

Wire.

Band.

Boston.

Arlington.

City.

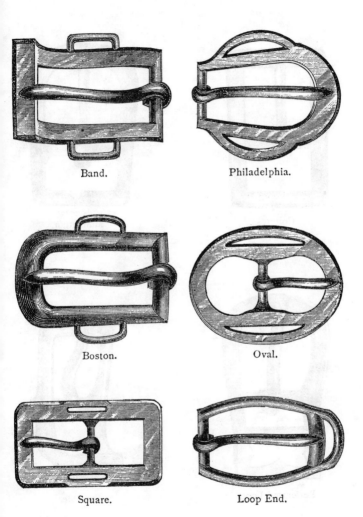

Band.

Philadelphia.

Boston.

Oval.

Square.

Loop End.

Congress.

Manhattan.

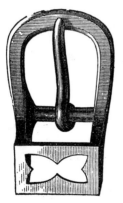

Perforated Loop.

Sensible.

CHAPTER XXII.

BITS AND BITTING HARNESS.

BRIDLE BITS.

THE ingenuity of bit makers of all countries has been taxed to the utmost to produce bits suited to all horses, and many are the harsh and brutal devices introduced; but with the exception of the Mexican or Texan bit, very few of the harsh kinds are now in use. For this reason no attention will be paid to any but those suited to the general trade. The illustrations show a good variety, but they all come under the general classification of snaffle, ring, bradoon, or lever.

The snaffle is frequently defined as a bit having a jointed mouth; this is incorrect, as the cheek piece alone decides the name, the mouth pieces being designated as stiff, jointed, post, chain, leather, hinge, etc. Figs. 1 and 2 illustrate two styles of snaffle. The first is the regular pattern; the second, the "Dexter;" both are made up with stiff as well as jointed mouths. The origin of the name is unknown; but when a bit maker receives an order for a "snaffle bit," he furnishes one with cheek pieces like that in Fig. 1, the ring and bars of which are of one piece; if a "Dexter" snaffle is ordered, it is like Fig. 2, the peculiarity

of which is the shape of the mouth piece, it being large at the cheek and small at the joint.

A ring bit is one having rings instead of rings
and cheek pieces combined. The portion, however, which is surrounded by the head on
the mouth piece is turned so as to give
a straight bearing and provide two shoulders,
which prevents the ring slipping through the
hole in the heads of the mouth piece. The bradoon bit has a ring cheek, but the wire is of uniform thickness, and the ring is loose in the ends
of the mouth piece. Lever, or gag, bits (as they
are generally called) are made up in a variety of
ornamental patterns, with stiff or loose cheeks.
The "Hanoverian," Fig. 3, is used more than any
other pattern. For coach or coupé harness the
"Buxton" is the most popular. This has a scroll
cheek and a loose mouth, which slides up and
down on a straight section of the cheek.

Trotting snaffles are made in a variety of patterns, and as a rule with half cheeks. The "Dan
Mace" is one of this class; the small loop on the
cheek piece is used to secure a cross strap, thus
connecting the two cheeks in such a manner that
they act together when either rein is pulled.
The "Ben Lane," "Dexter," and other half
cheek bits are also provided with the loop. The
various other patterns shown need no explanation.

Bits are made of wrought iron throughout,
wrought mouth and malleable cheeks, or all malleable. The first are sometimes designated as

steel bits; but this is a mere pretence, as steel is
seldom used in their manufacture, fine iron being
preferable. The wrought bit is the most expensive, but it is the only reliable kind, and no horse
possessing any spirit should be driven with any
other. Next to this is the wrought mouth and
malleable cheek; and lastly, the all malleable, a
bit which should never be used. Some are sufficiently strong, but the unreliability of malleable
iron should condemn it for bits of any kind.

A very convenient manner of numbering has
been adopted by some bit manufacturers, by
which a buyer can tell at a glance just what the
article is. If a buyer orders a No. 1336, he
would be furnished with a first quality ring bit
with a $\frac{6}{16}$ inch mouth piece, having two $1\frac{1}{2}$
inch rings. Should the number be 1356, he
would secure the same kind of bit with three inch
rings; for a loose ring bit the first and last numbers would be the same, with 24 as the pattern
number. Snaffles are designated by 52, and half
cheek of the regular pattern by 53, and "Han-
overians" by 76. A first quality loose ring bit
would be designated by No. 1246, a snaffle by
1526, a half cheek snaffle by 1536, and a "Hanoverian" by 1766, the first and last numbers being changed to designate quality and size. When
used first, the numbers 1, 2, 3, 4, etc., represent
the quality; the final numbers, 5, 6, 7, 8, and 9
give the size of the mouth pieces in sixteenths of
an inch; the addition of the fraction $\frac{1}{2}$ designates
a jointed mouth.

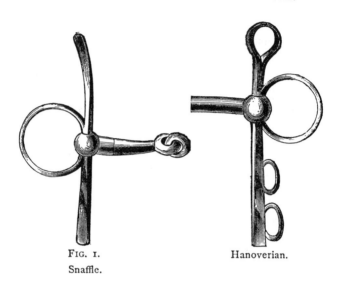

FIG. 1.
Snaffle.

Hanoverian.

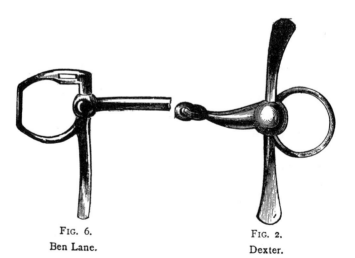

FIG. 6.
Ben Lane.

FIG. 2.
Dexter.

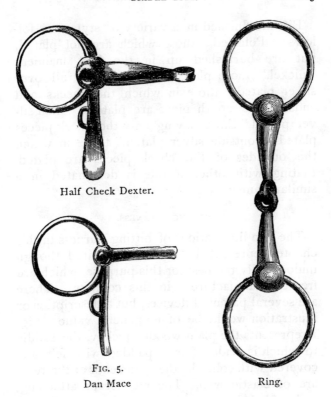

Half Check Dexter.

Fig. 5.
Dan Mace

Ring.

Check Bradoor.

Bits are finished in a variety of styles, as follows: " Polished," those which are not plated, but are burnished up in the best manner; "nickel," those plated with nickel; "all over silver plated," those in which the cheeks and ends of the mouth piece are plated; " half silver plated," those having only the cheek pieces plated; "outside silver plated," those in which the outsides of the cheek pieces are plated. Plating with other metals is designated in a similar manner.

BITTING HARNESS.

The two illustrations of bitting harness in this chapter represent the most complicated, though undoubtedly the best for this purpose, which are free to manufacturers in this country. There are several patented devices, but a description or illustration would be of no general value. Fig. 1 represents the plain wooden jockey, the saddle to which is made of iron padded with felt and covered with collar leather; the ends of the reins are of elastic web. The manner of attaching, style of halter, crupper strap, etc., are all well delineated and require no explanation. Fig. 2 represents an improved jockey of English manufacture; the arms of this are of gutta percha and whalebone instead of wood; the various straps are all provided with elastic ends, which, it is claimed, produces the desired result in a more humane manner than when the old style, as shown by Fig. 1, is used.

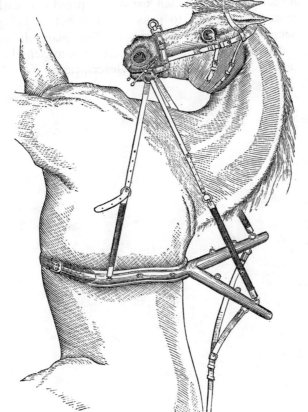

FIG. I.

Another style, bearing a close resemblance to Fig. 1, has steel springs attached to the back of the arms at the lower ends, to which the reins are attached ; the wooden arms are provided with slots for the reins to pass through before being secured to the steel springs. The plain bitting harness, in which the cheeks, etc., are attached to a broad surcingle, needs no description.

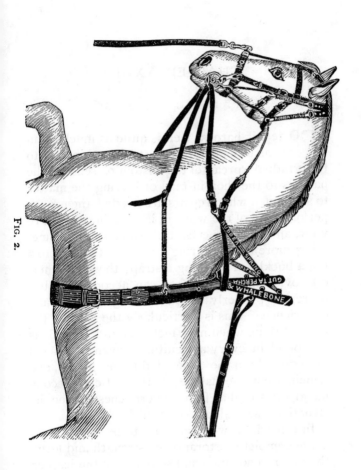

FIG. 2.

CHAPTER XXIII.

REPAIRING HARNESS.

TO repair harness well is quite as much of an
art as to make up new stock, and, owing to
the gradual spread of the custom of sending the
harness to the shop instead of leaving the matter
to stablemen when repairs are needed, the proper
performance of the work is, in a business point of
view, an absolute necessity. Repairing is something more than securing a ripped stitch, restoring a buckle, or splicing a strap; these the mer-
est novice in the business can accomplish; but
to repair properly requires skill, judgment, and
experience. This is particularly the case at the
present time, when new methods and directions
are found in every agricultural journal, and not
unfrequently in those devoted to mechanics, and
which, from the nature of the articles recommended, as well as from the crudeness of the instructions, are calculated to mislead.

In repairing, two results are to be sought—one
is the complete restoration of strength and form;
the other, renovation and softening of the leather,
so that in appearance and pliability it will be as
nearly as possible what it was when first made. To

do this, unbuckle and separate all patent and fancy colored from the plain leather wherever it can be done without ripping; also from pads, gig saddles, and such other parts as are lined with cloth or are stuffed; then clean the straps. These, if gummed, should be scraped with a smooth edged scraper, and then washed with tepid water and crown soap; if the latter can not be had, use castile soap in its place (strong soap should never be used, as the alkalies penetrate the leather and harden it). Turpentine, benzine, etc., are often recommended for removing the surface grease and accumulated dirt; but nothing will more effectually destroy harness leather than these articles: they penetrate almost instantly, and burn and harden the fibre, and if used to any extent, the injury can not be corrected. Tepid water, soap, a scraper, and a little labor will prove equally efficacious in removing all superfluous substances, without leaving injurious effects.

After thoroughly cleaning the leather, make all needed repairs, black up, and, with the exception of polishing, treat the leather the same as though the harness were new; then with a stiff brush clean out whatever dirt may be in and around the stitches, loops, buckles, etc., treating both sides of the strap in the same manner. This brushing is often omitted, but it is almost as important as the cleaning of the surface of the leather, as the fine dirt is thus removed, and it does not interfere in any way with the penetration of the oil or grease into the pores of the leather or around the stitches.

The harness now being cleaned and repaired, it is ready for oiling or greasing. There are two ways of doing this: the first, which is applicable to leather which has become hard, lost its color, and needs thorough renovation, is to apply a little vinegar black wherever the leather appears red; then dampen each strap with a small quantity of tepid water, applying it with a sponge, and, as soon as the surface of the leather is dry, give it a coat of pure neat's-foot oil (the purer the oil the better); the oil penetrates the leather, the water having opened the pores, and it is quickly absorbed. Some authorities recommend castor oil in place of the neat's-foot, but the latter is undoubtedly the best, as it restores to the leather some of its natural properties, and therefore better assimilates with the fibre. Castor oil, however, is an excellent article, and is only inferior to neat's-foot or pure cod. It penetrates rapidly, softens well, and at the same time retains a firm hold; it will also last as long as neat's-foot oil, and is free from gum, but, owing to its heavy body, it fills up the pores and thus prevents the subsequent absorption of tallow. The animal oil, on the other hand, opens the pores, softens the fibre, and fits it to take up a much greater quantity of tallow, which is, after all, the only real protection against the action of water. The tallow should be warmed sufficiently to allow of its being spread on with a brush, but it must not be hot. Apply it as soon as the oil has dried in, and brush well in order to assist it to enter the pores. Lay all the straps out straight, and, after coating them with tallow, allow them to remain in that condition for several hours; then rub them with a woolen cloth until all surplus grease is removed from the surface, after which varnish black may be applied if desired; but the latter is not absolutely necessary, excepting when the leather is much worn and the color injured.

The second manner of applying grease is to slightly dampen the leather after it has been thoroughly cleaned, and as soon as the surface moisture is removed, apply a coat of warm tallow, and allow the straps to remain coated with it until the moisture has died out, afterward cleaning the tallow off as in the first case. This answers very well for harness when the leather has not become hard but looks dry on the surface. In the absence of grease, leather absorbs water very rapidly, and unless the pores be well filled with the former, the latter will soon obtain the mastery and convert the leather from a soft, pliant, tough material to a hard, bony, and brittle one.

Tallow of itself will resist the action of water much longer than neat's-foot oil, but it does not impart the same softness to the fibre as does the latter, while the oil, though it softens the leather, fails to form much of a barrier against the entrance of water. Both articles are therefore necessary in order to secure pliability and durability. Other greases may be used, but in none are the original qualities of the leather contained to the same extent as in those recommended.

When the leather presents a rusty appearance, but is not red, it should be blacked with hatters' black, or a more simple black made of 2 ounces of the extract of logwood and ½ ounce of bichromate of potash pounded fine and dissolved in 4 quarts of boiling rain or river water. This can be bottled and kept on hand. It should be applied with a brush.

Harness when in use becomes soiled either by the action of the atmosphere on the grease—the latter being drawn to the surface, where it becomes impregnated with dust, and forms a dirty coating—or by the impurities in the oil used in currying the leather. In the latter case, in addition to the dirty grease, spots of gum of various sizes form on the surface. These can only be removed by scraping, or by the use of an ammoniated soap, made of oleic acid heated to a temperature of 100°, into which ammonia (of 0.96 specific gravity) is stirred until the smell of the latter ceases to disappear by action of the acid.

Patent leather can only be restored to its original polish by the use of varnish, but it may be greatly improved by applying castor oil, and, after it has been upon the leather an hour or more, removing the surplus grease with a woolen cloth, and rubbing with a dry silk or woolen rag until the polish is brought out. In every case remove all the mountings possible without ripping the straps, and clean them before replacing.

It requires some labor to thus clean, repair, and oil a harness, but these directions, if well followed, will secure a first class job, and if the leather has not become bony and harsh from constant exposure, it will be to all appearances as good as new.

For repairing or new work there is no blacking in the market that answers the purpose better than that of Frank Miller & Co. It possesses the necessary elements for softening and giving a fine finish to the leather, and increasing its durability.

CHAPTER XXIV.

CARE OF HARNESS IN FACTORY AND STABLE.

THE appearance and durability of harness to a great extent depends upon the treatment received after leaving the hands of the workman; yet a large percentage of manufacturers, as well as consumers, are very careless and negligent in protecting their goods from injury by the elements. Consumers, as a rule, are entirely unacquainted with the peculiarities of the stock used, and they can not, therefore, be expected to know how to guard it against various destructive influences, but the harness maker can not plead ignorance. Leather as received from the tanner does not possess the requisite qualifications for harness. These the currier supplies by the addition of oil and grease, together with the labor needed in preparing it, without which it would lack the suppleness and durability so necessary in this kind of stock. The preservation of the materials added by the currier, therefore, becomes an absolute necessity in order to prevent premature decay.

Moisture is the great destroyer; it absorbs the grease, hardens the fibre, and renders the leather weak and brittle; it also causes the metal in the mountings to rust, weakening them, and adds another enemy to the leather. Grease only will resist the effects of moisture, and every effort should be made to keep the leather well supplied with this needed protector.

Manufacturers often overlook the importance of caring for the harness in stock, and also of instructing their customers how to preserve it when in use. With some the idea is maintained, that ignorance on the part of the consumer, as regards the care of harness, accrues to the benefit of the manufacturer. This is a serious mistake. The most successful man is he who produces the most durable article, and it should be part of a manufacturer's duty to instruct the buyer how to treat the article purchased. But all manufacturers do not understand this secret of their business, and a portion of this chapter therefore will be devoted to the care of stock in the warerooms.

A certain amount of made up stock must be displayed, but there is no necessity for exposing more than one harness of a kind. Three months' exposure in a wareroom will injure a harness as much as three months of constant use, providing the user knows how to take care of it. In all instances leather strapping, if exposed at all, should be in glass cases impervious to dust and air; but no showcase can be made tight enough to fully exclude these elements.

During a great part of the year the air at night is laden with moisture, and, not unfrequently, during the spring and fall months the atmos-

phere is humid and heavy; the moist air per-
meates every thing, and by its action upon the
leather and mountings rapidly absorbs the life
of the former and rusts or tarnishes the latter.
The white mould which is often observed upon
the leather is caused by the grease being drawn
to the surface by moisture. After the surface is
covered with this mould, the absorption of the
grease continues in all kinds of weather until the
cause is removed. The manufacturer therefore
should remove it as quickly as possible by brushing it, and afterwards rubbing with a dry cloth,
and finally with a greasy rag or "shammy;" then
restore the polish with an old silk handkerchief.
If the mountings are tarnished, clean them with a
"shammy;" if this can not be done, remove them
clean with a little rotten stone. Gilt mountings
should not be exposed. Sample sets are convenient; but when these can not be had, the gilt
should be protected by wrapping it in tissue
paper.

In hanging up the various parts of the harness,
use forms, instead of pegs or hooks, except for
traces or reins, which should always be hung out
straight. Harness made up for stock should not
be "gummed" and hung in cases, but, after being
finished by the workman, all the plain leather
should be covered with a thin coat of "daub"
made of one part of neat's-foot oil and two parts
of tallow—the latter being thoroughly melted,
after which the oil is poured in and the whole
thoroughly stirred until cold;—this will feed the

leather and prevent injury. The patent and fancy leather should be wrapped on soft paper, and every piece, whether of patent or plain leather, laid out straight and smooth in shallow drawers and covered with thick paper. Russet strapping of all kinds should be kept in dark cases or drawers, as the sunlight is sure to affect the color, the most exposed parts showing the greatest change.

Harness makers who have made the care of harness a study have no difficulty in filling orders at a short notice. Their course is to make up traces, reins, turnbacks, docks, back bands, and other straight strapping, and lay them away in grease as before directed. When a harness is ordered, all that is required is to make the other parts, finish up the necessary straight straps, attach the mountings, and put them together. In this way they are enabled to keep their workmen employed at all times, and obviate the necessity of hiring extra hands in the busy season. If the manufacturer delivers the harness to his customer in good order, he does all he is legally bound to do; but his moral obligation extends much farther—he should instruct the buyer how to preserve it. The following hints may serve to assist him in this direction :

The harness room should always be as far from the horses as the size of the building will allow, as the gases arising from the stable are very injurious to the leather and mountings ; it should be provided with forms for the bridles, pads, saddles, breechings, etc., and hooks for reins, hames, and traces. If a separate room can not be had for this purpose, closets should be provided.

Harness are often quite wet when taken from the horse. When this is caused by rain, hang them up in some place where they can dry, and before putting them in the storeroom rub them well with a "shammy," or wash-leather, then apply a little crown soap and rub with the hands until the polish is restored ; clean off the under side of the straps as carefully as the outside. If wet by sweat, dry as quickly as possible after taking them from the horse, as by the saline nature of the perspiration the grease is rapidly absorbed and the leather hardened ; if the pads are wet, dry them thoroughly before putting them in the storeroom. For oiling, during the first year, at least, crown soap, applied as directed above, is all that is requisite for coach or carriage harness, but for team and other heavy harness a stronger grease is required. Cleaning and oiling should be done as often as once a month on harness which is in daily use. If the leather is soft, wash it with water applied with a " shammy," then wring the latter nearly dry, and rub the leather thoroughly, after which apply a good harness oil. When each strap has been treated in this way, commence with the one first washed, and remove all surplus grease with a rag, then rub with an old piece of silk until the polish is restored. If the leather is hard and dry, it will be necessary to wash the straps well and wet them enough to open the pores ; lay the straps out straight, and, when surface dry apply a coat of neat's-foot oil. When this has penetrated the leather, apply warm tallow with a brush, and allow the straps to remain coated with the tallow until the moisture has dried out of the leather, then with a rag remove all the surplus tallow, and clean the stitching with a stiff brush; then apply a coat of harness black.

Cleaning mountings requires care, as they do not need to be scoured. Gold should never be rubbed with any thing harsher than the nap side of canton flannel ; electro silver plate should also be cleaned carefully, as the plate is soft and the thin coating can be easily removed. Close plate silver will bear more scouring, but it is seldom necessary to do more than to rub it with a "shammy" darkened with tripoli and lampblack. If they are very much tarnished, they should be removed from the harness and washed in water and rubbed with tripoli. Brass is the most difficult metal to keep clean, but when rubbed each day the labor is materially decreased. In the chapter of recipes there are several directions for cleaning and polishing brass, any of which can be used to good advantage.

CHAPTER XXV.

LEATHER BLACKING — STAINS — VARNISHES AND POLISHES.

VINEGAR BLACK.

FOR giving color to the grain of leather there is no blacking that will at all compare with the well known vinegar black. This may be made in various ways. The simplest, and, without doubt, the best, is to procure shavings from an iron turner and cover them with pure cider vinegar; heat up and set aside for a week or two, then heat again and set in a cool place for two weeks; pour off the vinegar, allow it to stand for a few days, and draw off and cork up in bottles. This will keep for a long time, and, while producing a deep black on leather, will not stain the hands.

Another method is to cover iron scraps with sour beer, and allow them to stand for a month or more; then strain off the beer and bottle as before. A third method is to boil sulphate of iron in vinegar; mix some brewers' yeast with beer and allow it to stand for twenty-four hours, then skim off the yeast and add the vinegar.

LOGWOOD BLACK.

Boil 1 pound of ground logwood, ½ pound of nut galls, and 1 ounce of verdigris in 1 gallon of water for two hours, then remove from the fire and allow it to stand until it is cold; strain off the liquor, and it will be ready for use.

If to 1 pint of this mixture be added ¼ pound of white wax, ½ pound of brown sugar, and ½ pound of bone black rubbed smooth in turpentine, and the whole heated until thoroughly amalgamated, an excellent wax for finishing edges will be produced.

Another logwood black is made by boiling a quantity of logwood bark in double its bulk of rain water for two or three hours, then straining off and adding ¼ of a pound of potash to 2 gallons of the liquor. This makes a good grain as well as edge black.

HATTERS' BLACK.

This black is unequaled for finishing. It is made by dissolving 1 pound of extract of logwood, ½ ounce of bichromate of potash, and 1 ounce of copperas in 1 gallon of water.

Another formula, differing from the first in the quantities, is to dissolve 1 pound of extract of logwood, 2 ounces of copperas, and 1½ ounces of bichromate of potash in 1½ gallons of water.

BALL BLACK.

Melt together 8 ounces of beef suet, 2 ounces of neat's-foot oil, 2 ounces of white wax, and 2 ounces of pulverized gum arabic; add 1 gill of turpentine, and a sufficient quantity of bone black to give the whole a good color; stir until thoroughly mixed, remove from the fire, continue to stir until cold, then roll into balls. To apply, warm the ball, rub it on the leather, and polish with a woolen cloth.

English ball blacking for harness is composed of 1 ounce of lard, 1 ounce of beeswax, 8 ounces of ivory black, 8 ounces of sugar, 4 ounces of linseed oil, and 2 or 3 ounces of water.

Another kind is made of 2 ounces of hog's lard, 8 ounces of best neat's-foot oil, 2 ounces of beeswax, 10 ounces of ivory black, and 8 ounces of water. Heat the whole to a boil, remove from the fire, stir until sufficiently cool, and form into balls about two inches in diameter.

A third description is made of 2 ounces each of ivory black, copperas, and neat's-foot oil, 4 ounces of brown sugar, 4 ounces of soft water, and 1 ounce of gum tragacanth ; boil until the water has evaporated, stir until cold, then roll into balls or mould into cakes.

A fourth is made of $\frac{1}{2}$ pound of beeswax, 4 ounces of ivory black, 2 ounces of Prussian blue, 2 ounces of spirits of turpentine, and 1 ounce of copal varnish ; melt the wax, stir in the other ingredients, and, when cool, roll into balls.

Still another famous harness and saddlery blacking is made of $\frac{1}{4}$ of an ounce of isinglass, $\frac{1}{4}$ of an ounce of indigo, 4 ounces of logwood, 2 ounces of softsoap, 4 ounces of glue, and 1 pint of vinegar ; the whole is warmed, mixed, strained, allowed to cool, and is then ready for use.

LIQUID BLACK.

Mix a quantity of bone black with equal parts of neat's-foot oil and brown sugar, in proportions to produce a thick paste; thin with vinegar and sulphuric acid in proportions of three parts of the former to one of the latter.

A second liquid black is made by mixing 3 ounces of ivory black with 1 tablespoonful of lemon acid, 2 ounces of brown sugar, and a small quantity of vinegar, afterward adding 1 ounce each of sulphuric and muriatic acid; mix the whole together, and add a sufficient quantity of vinegar to make 1 pint in all.

LIEBIG'S BLACK.

Mix bone black in half its weight of molasses and one eighth its weight of olive oil, to which add half its weight of hydrochloric acid and one fourth its weight of strong sulphuric acid, with a sufficient quantity of water to produce a thin paste.

PATENT HARNESS BLACK.

Heat together, over a slow fire, 2 ounces of white wax and 3 ounces of turpentine; when the wax is dissolved add 1 ounce of ivory black and 1 dram of indigo, thoroughly pulverized and mixed; stir the mixture until cold. Apply with a cloth, and polish with a shoe brush.

WATERPROOF PASTE BLACKING.

Melt together 4 ounces of black resin and 6

ounces of beeswax over a slow fire; when thoroughly dissolved, add 1 ounce of lampblack and ¼ pound of finely powdered Prussian blue; stir the mixture well, and add sufficient turpentine to make a thin paste. Apply with a cloth, and polish with a brush.

CROWN SOAP BLACK.

Dissolve, over a slow fire, 1 pound of beeswax, 1 pound of crown soap, 3 ounces of indigo, 4 ounces of ivory black, and ½ pint of oil of turpentine; as soon as dissolved remove from the fire, and stir until cold.

FINISHING BLACK.

Mix together ½ ounce each of gelatin and indigo, 8 ounces of extract of logwood, 2 ounces of crown soap, 8 ounces of softened glue, and 1 quart of vinegar; heat the whole over a slow fire, and stir until thoroughly mixed. Apply with a soft brush, and polish with a woolen cloth.

CORDOVA WAX.

Mix together 1½ pints of red acid (chromic), 1 pint of beer, 1 gill of thick glue, 2 ounces of ivory black, and 1 dram of indigo; boil for half an hour, and apply with a sponge.

GERMAN BLACKING.

Soften 2 pounds of good glue, and melt it in an ordinary glue kettle; then dissolve 2 pounds of castile soap in warm water and pour it into the glue; stir until well mixed, and add ½ pound of yellow wax cut into small pieces; stir well until the wax is melted, then add ¼ pint of neat's-foot oil and enough lampblack to give the desired color. When thoroughly mixed, it is ready for use.

ANILIN BLACK.

Mix 1 dram of fine anilin black with 60 drops of concentrated hydrochloric acid and 1½ ounces of alcohol. This produces a deep blue liquid, which, when diluted with 1½ ounces of shellac dissolved in alcohol, will produce a beautiful black.

BLACKING FOR RESTORING HARNESS.

Mix 1 ounce of indigo, 1 pound of extract of logwood, 1 ounce of softened glue, and 8 ounces of crown soap (common softsoap can be used if the other kind can not be had) in 2 quarts of vinegar; place the mass over a slow fire, and stir until thoroughly mixed. Apply with a soft brush, and use a harder one for polishing.

BLACKING FOR PATENT OR ENAMELED LEATHER.

Mix together ½ pound each of ivory black, purified lampblack, and pulverized indigo, 3 ounces of dissolved gum arabic, 4 ounces of brown sugar, and ¼ ounce of glue dissolved in 1 pint of water; heat the whole to a boil over a slow fire, then remove and stir until cool, and roll into balls.

BLACKING FOR RESTORING LEATHER COVERED MOUNTINGS.

Melt 3 parts of white wax, then add 1 part gum copal, dissolved in linseed oil, and 1 part of ivory black; allow the mass to boil for five minutes, remove it from the fire and stir until cool, then roll it up into balls.

BLACKING FOR THE FLESH SIDE.

Mix together 1 pound of prime lampblack and 12 pounds of pure neat's-foot oil; melt 6 pounds of good tallow, and add it while hot to the lampblack and oil. Mix it well, and when cold it will be fit for use.

ANOTHER.

To 1½ pounds of lampblack add 1 gallon of pure neat's-foot oil and 1 quart of vinegar black; allow it to stand 24 hours, and it will be ready for use.

STAINS.

The use of russet and brown leather for reins, etc., necessitates the employment of stains of various shades in the workshop, in order that the reins or other straps may be of a uniform color after being worked. In most cases rein leather is stained by the currier, but when worked, the freshly cut edges, etc., need to be stained to correspond with the grain. The stains used are generally made of Spanish saffron and anotta, or of saffron alone, made up in various ways, the most common and reliable being the following:

Boil a given amount of saffron in water until the color is extracted; cut a quantity of anotta in urine and mix the two together, the proportions of each determining the shade; the more anotta used the darker is the color.

Another manner of preparing this stain is to boil $\frac{1}{2}$ ounce of Spanish saffron and $\frac{1}{4}$ ounce of anotta in water until the dye is extracted, to which must be added some alcohol to set the color.

To make a stain of saffron alone, boil a quantity in water until the dye is extracted; strain off, and, when cold, add alcohol in order to set the color. The shade may be changed by adding oxalic acid in varying quantities according to the color required. The proportions can not be given with any degree of accuracy, as the color is a matter of taste, and can be regulated by using greater or less proportions of each article.

Another saffron stain is made by boiling saffron in a small quantity of water until the color is extracted, and reducing with urine.

In using any of these stains, apply them with a cloth, and, when nearly dry, rub with a woolen rag slightly waxed.

A yellow stain is produced by boiling fustic berries in alum water; the shade may be darkened by the addition of a small quantity of powdered Brazilwood boiled with the berries.

Another yellowish red stain is made of Brazilwood and yellow berries in proportion to suit, boiling them in water until the coloring matter is extracted. This can be applied to sides that have not been stained, when intended for flat reins, halters, etc., in the following manner :

Lay the leather upon a table, and rub the flesh side with a warm stretching iron; turn it over and moisten the grain side with water, and rub with a copper stretching iron until the leather is nearly dry ; then apply the coloring matter to the grain, and rub with a copper slicker. When the leather is perfectly dry, rub the grain with a glass slicker. An edge stain is made by adding a small quantity of alum to the above mentioned ingredients.

A brown stain is made by boiling equal parts of pine and alder barks in six times their bulk of water until all the coloring matter is extracted, and when cold adding a small quantity of alcohol. Saffron boiled for twelve or fifteen hours gives a good brown stain, to which alcohol must be added to make it set.

Picric acid and water, in proportions of 1 to 10, heated to a blood heat, makes a good yellow stain. Wold boiled in water also makes a yellow stain.

An orange yellow is produced by boiling fustic berries in alum water. This stain may be converted into a rich brown by washing the leather to which it has been applied, before the stain is fairly dry, with an alkali.

A red stain is produced by boiling Brazilwood in lye. If mixed with wold, it produces a brownish yellow, well adapted for use on halters and bridles.

An edge stain for russet leather is made by cutting 4 ounces of anotta in 2 quarts of urine, allowing it to stand for twenty-four hours, then adding 3 quarts of water and boiling until reduced to one half the original quantity.

All stains appear to better advantage and are rendered more durable by being covered with a little shellac varnish, which should be applied after the reins are all dry, and then finished up as previously directed. The shellac should be applied with a sponge.

A bright orange stain is made by mixing yellow anilin with alum water.

One ounce of oxalic acid, 1 ounce of spirits of salts, 1 scruple of bruised cochineal, and 1 pint of boiling water makes a good brown stain.

Another red stain is made by dissolving 1 ounce of cochineal in ½ pint of hot water, and adding 1 gill of spirits of hartshorn.

A bright crimson stain is alum or tin salts and a decoction of cochineal.

VARNISHES.

SHELLAC VARNISH.

Dissolve 6 parts of shellac in alcohol using no more of the latter than is absolutely necessary to dissolve the gum, and mix it with 3 parts of Venetian turpentine, heating the whole

until the mixture is complete ; when cool, add
½ part of fine bone black and ½ part of oil
of lavender (all the parts by weight). Mix
the mass in a druggist's mortar, and rub smooth ;
then add turpentine enough to reduce it to the
proper consistency.

ELASTIC VARNISH.

Dissolve ½ pound of gum caoutchouc in ether,
and when thoroughly cut, add ½ pound each of
linseed oil and spirits of turpentine ; boil over a
slow fire until the mixture becomes clear, strain
it, and when cold it is ready for use. To harden
it and make it dry quicker, use one half the quantity of gum caoutchouc, and substitute the best
gum copal for the remainder.

GERMAN LEATHER VARNISH.

Pulverize a quantity of the best copal gum, and
add enough turpentine to moisten it; place it in a
glazed vessel, and allow it to stand over a moderate fire until the gum is thoroughly dissolved,
which will require about ten hours. Next take
double the quantity of linseed oil that there is
of the gum and turpentine combined, and heat
it ; when nearly to a boil, pour in the dissolved
gum, and allow it to remain over the fire until
it has reached as high a degree of temperature
as it will bear with safety, stirring it all the
while ; then remove from the fire, and when it
has cooled a little, thin with spirits of turpentine until the proper consistency is reached.

strain through a fine cloth, bottle it, and set it in the sun to ripen. This is an excellent varnish for horse collars. If used upon those that have lost their color, a little bone black should be added.

LACK VARNISH BALLS.

Melt together 2 ounces of white wax and 6 ounces of beef tallow; add ½ pint of turpentine, 8 ounces of ivory black, 2 ounces of Prussian blue ground in linseed oil, and allow the mass to boil for about five minutes; then remove it from the fire and add 4 ounces of shellac varnish, stir the mass until cool, and roll into balls.

BLACK VARNISH.

Pulverize and mix together 1½ parts of mastic, 2½ parts of shellac, 2½ parts of dragon's blood, and 2 parts of the best bone black; heat 1½ parts of turpentine and 10 parts of alcohol, pour them over the gums, place the whole over a moderate fire, and boil until the latter are thoroughly dissolved.

WATERPROOF VARNISH.

Pulverize 1 pound of shellac, and put it into a bottle with a sufficient quantity of alcohol to cover the gum; cork the bottle tightly, and keep it in a warm place until the gum is dissolved. To a quart of the liquid add 1 ounce of ivory black and ½ ounce of gum camphor dissolved in alcohol. Apply with a varnish brush. If too thick to work well, thin with alcohol.

BLACK VARNISH FOR JAPANNED WORK.

Dissolve 2 pounds of asphaltum in 1 pint of boiled linseed oil ; heat in an iron pot until thoroughly fused, then remove from the fire, and, when cooled off a little, add 2 quarts of spirits of turpentine, and stir until cold. Apply with a brush. This makes an excellent japan for retouching japanned mountings, seats, etc., that have been injured by the japan scaling off.

CHEAP SHELLAC VARNISH.

Dissolve asphaltum in turpentine, using no more of the latter than is absolutely necessary ; add a small quantity of bone black and enough shellac varnish to reduce it so that it can be applied with a brush. Spread it very thinly.

ELASTIC VARNISH.

Equal parts of gum caoutchouc and copal, the former dissolved in ether, heated in a vessel until thoroughly dissolved, with enough linseed oil added while hot to reduce it to the proper consistency, makes an elastic varnish well suited for finishing collars.

POLISHES.

FRENCH POLISH.

Beat 5 pounds of stearin out into thin sheets with a wooden mallet, and mix with 7 pounds of oil of turpentine, after which subject the mass to

a water bath, and heat up; when hot, add ½ ounce
of ivory or bone black, stirring well to prevent
crystallization. To cool it off, it should be emptied into another vessel and stirred until cold.
To use, warm it until it is reduced to a liquid
state, and apply in small quantities with a cloth;
afterward rub it well with a piece of silk or linen
cloth to bring up the polish.

POLISH FOR PATENT LEATHER.

Mix together the whites of two eggs, 1 tea-
spoonful of spirits of wine, 1 ounce of sugar, and
as much finely pulverized ivory black as may be
required to produce the necessary shade of black.
Apply with a sponge, and polish with a piece of
silk.

WAX POLISH.

Melt together 1 pound of white wax, 1 pound
of crown soap, 5 ounces of ivory black, 1 ounce
of indigo, and ½ pint of nut oil; dissolve over a
slow fire, stir until cool, and turn into small
moulds.

LIQUID POLISH.

Melt 2 pounds of wax, and add ¼ pound of
washed and well dried litharge by screening it
through a fine sieve; then add 6 ounces of ivory
black, and stir until cool, but not cold; add
enough turpentine to reduce it to a thin paste,
after which add a little birch or other essential
oil to prevent it from souring.

GERMAN LEATHER POLISH.

Soften 1 part of white glue in water, add 3 parts of crown soap, and heat the whole over a slow fire until the glue is thoroughly dissolved; moisten 3 parts of bone black with vinegar, and mix it with 1 part of wheat starch beat smooth in cold water; mix the whole, and allow it to stand over a slow fire for half an hour, stirring it all the time, then turn it into another kettle and stir until it is cold. To use, dissolve a small quantity in sour beer or vinegar, and apply with a brush, spreading it as thinly as possible.

CHAPTER XXVI.

MISCELLANEOUS RECIPES FOR THE WORKSHOP AND HARNESS ROOM.

TO CLEAN MOULDY LEATHERS.

REMOVE the surface mould with a dry cloth, and with another cloth apply pyroligneous acid. Leather that has been badly moulded can be restored in this way.

TO PROTECT HARNESS FROM RATS.

Apply a plentiful coat of castor oil. If the harness is to be used, add tallow in the proportions of about one third of the latter to two thirds oil.

WATERPROOF OIL.

Take of lard oil 100 parts, paraffin 50 parts, beeswax 5 parts; heat the oil over a slow fire, and when hot add the paraffin and wax; allow the whole to remain over the fire until the latter articles are melted, and add a few drops of oil of sassafras or other essential oil to preserve it.

CROWN SOAP.

This soap, so much used by stablemen for cleaning harness, is made of whale or cod oil, lye of potassa, and a small quantity of tallow. The oil gives to the soap a dark brown color, the tallow forming white granulations. This is simply the Scotch softsoap; it can be produced at a price far below that asked for the imported article.

BELGIUM BURNISHING POWDER.

Mix together $\frac{1}{2}$ pound of fine chalk, 3 ounces of pipe clay, 2 ounces of dry white lead, $\frac{3}{4}$ of an ounce of carbonate of magnesia, and $\frac{3}{4}$ of an ounce of rouge.

POWDER FOR CLEANING SILVER.

Mix together 1 ounce of fine chalk, 2 ounces of cream of tartar, 1 ounce of rotten stone, 1 ounce of red lead, and $\frac{1}{2}$ ounce of alum, and pulverize thoroughly in a mortar. Wet the mixture and rub it on the silver, and, when dry, rub off with a dry flannel, or clean with a small brush.

POWDER FOR CLEANING BRASS MOUNTINGS.

Make a paste of equal parts of sulphur and chalk, with sufficient vinegar to reduce it to the proper consistency. Apply it to the metal while moist, allow it to dry on, and rub with chamois skin. For ornaments or engraved work, clean with a brush.

Another process, and one that gives to the brass a very brilliant color, is to make a wash of alum boiled in strong lye, in the proportion of 1 ounce of alum to 1 pint of the latter. Wash the brass with this mixture, and afterward rub with shammy and tripoli.

A weak solution of ammonia in water makes an excellent wash for cleaning tarnished silver plate. Apply it with a rag, dry with a piece of shammy, and afterward rub with a piece of shammy and a very small quantity of jewelers' rouge.

PREPARED CHALK.

Pulverize chalk thoroughly, and mix with distilled water in the proportion of 2 pounds to the gallon ; stir well, and then allow it to stand about two minutes, during which time the gritty matter will have settled to the bottom ; then pour the chalky water into another vessel, being careful not to disturb the sediment, and allow the fine chalk to settle to the bottom ; pour off the water, and place the chalk in a warm oven to dry. This is an excellent powder for restoring silver, and it is also useful as a base for other polishing powders.

Spanish whiting treated in the same manner, with a small quantity of jewelers' rouge added, makes a powder that is a little sharper than the prepared chalk, and which is well adapted to cleaning polished steel articles.

A third powder, and one that is still sharper

than either of the above, is made of rotten stone treated in the same manner as the chalk. The addition of bone black to any of these powders will prevent their discoloring the leather.

TO PREVENT STEEL BITS FROM RUSTING.

Polished steel bits, chains, etc., whether in packages or in showcases, may be preserved from rust by dusting them over with quicklime. Those in use should be placed in a box nearly filled with thoroughly pulverized slaked lime immediately after being removed from the horse. The lime absorbs the moisture, and thus prevents rust. Before using, rub well with a woolen cloth. Polished steel, when covered with red rust, may be cleaned as follows : Cover the article with oil, and rub it with a woolen cloth to remove the lighter portion of the rust, after which apply another coat of oil, and allow it to remain undisturbed for two or three hours, then clean off with whiting and a woolen cloth. If the rust has been upon the steel sufficiently long to have eaten into the metal, the surface can be restored only by the use of the emery belt or wheel.

TO CLEAN RUBBER COVERED MOUNTINGS.

Rub the covered as well as the metallic parts with a shammy and a little tripoli, and finish with a clean woolen cloth.

TO CLEAN RUSSET LEATHER COVERED MOUNTINGS.

Remove all stains and dirt by rubbing the

leather with a cloth and a little oxalic acid, and restore the color and finish by the use of salts of lemon, applied with a woolen cloth. Rub the leather until a good polish is produced.

VARNISH FOR COLLARS.

Digest shellac 12 parts, white turpentine 5 parts, gum sandarac 2 parts, lampblack 1 part, spirits of turpentine and alcohol each 40 parts.

TO CLEAN CELLULOID COVERED MOUNTINGS.

Rub the covered parts with a woolen cloth and a little tripoli, and polish with a clean woolen rag.

POLISHING LIQUID FOR OROIDE OR BRASS.

Place 2 ounces of sulphuric acid in an earthen vessel, and add 1 quart of cold soft water; after the heat that is generated has passed off, add 1 ounce each of tripoli and jewelers' rouge. When well mixed, put in a bottle for use.

TO CLEAN GILT MOUNTINGS.

Gilt mountings unless carefully cleaned soon lose their lustre. They should not be rubbed; if slightly tarnished, wipe them off with a piece of canton flannel, or, what is better, remove them from the harness and wash in a solution of ½ ounce of borax in 1 pound of water, and dry them with a soft linen rag. Their lustre may be improved by heating them a little and rubbing with a piece of canton flannel or a soft polishing brush.

TO CLEAN RIDING SADDLES.

If much soiled, wash the leather with a weak solution of oxalic acid and water, and, when dry, with the watery portion of beef blood. The latter can be preserved by adding a little carbolic acid, and keeping it in a bottle tightly corked.

TO CLEAN STEEL BITS.

Steel bits that are tarnished, but not rusty, can be cleaned with rotten stone, common hard soap, and a woolen cloth.

TO FINISH THE EDGES OF RUSSET REINS.

Use salts of tartar and water. If discolored, first remove the stain with a weak solution of oxalic acid.

TO CLEAN BROWN RIDING SADDLES.

Saddles may be cleaned to look as well as new by the use of tepid water and crown soap ; if the latter can not be had, use pure castile soap.

TO STAIN REIN LEATHER.

A rich permanent brown can be imparted to rein leather by treating the hides, after they are tanned, to a bath in a liquor made from equal parts of pine and alder bark. The hides are spread in a vat, with liquor enough to cover them, where they are allowed to remain one week; they are then removed, and fresh liquor is applied; by repeating this treatment three or four times, a very rich brown can be produced. Orange brown is produced by scraping the flesh side after the hides have been removed from the vats for the last time, and sprinkling them on the scraped side with pulverized alum. As soon as each one is sprinkled with the alum, it is laid in another vat, one upon the other, and allowed to remain twenty-four hours; they are then moistened with the alum liquor in the bottom of the vat, and laid upon the beam and well worked, after which they are rubbed with salt and alum, and rolled up and allowed to remain undisturbed for twenty-four hours; this salting is repeated three times, after which the hides are stretched lengthwise and dried; they are then boarded and worked soft, and treated to a coat of hog's lard and train oil on the flesh side; in about two days they are again boarded, and worked off with a glass slicker. This leather has a fine grain, and retains its softness for a long time.

SMEARY GREASE FOR RUSSET LEATHER.

Mix together 1 part of palm oil and 3 parts of common soap, and heat up to 100°; then add 4 parts of oleic acid and $1\frac{3}{4}$ parts of tanning solution containing at least $\frac{1}{16}$ part of tannic acid (all parts by weight), and stir until cold. This is recommended as a valuable grease for russet leather, and as a preventive of gumming.

TO SEPARATE SIDES OF PATENT LEATHER.

Patent and enameled leather will, if the glazed sides are placed together in warm weather, become stuck together, and, unless carefully separated, the leather will be spoiled. The simplest and best way to separate sides is to place them in a drying or other hot room ; when hot, they can be taken apart without injury to the glazed or enameled surface. If a drying room is not accessible, lay the sides on a tin roof on a hot day, and they will soon become heated sufficiently to allow their being separated without injury. Any attempt to separate without heating to a high degree will prove a failure.

TO CURRY RUSSET LEATHER.

The hide to be curried is placed upon a table, and a warm iron is rubbed over the flesh side ; it is then turned over, and the grain side is moistened with water and rubbed with a copper slicker until it is nearly dry, after which coloring matter, made of Brazilwood and yellow berries, is applied to the grain, and it is once more rubbed with the slicker; it is then spread out to dry, and the final finish is given by rubbing the grain with a glass slicker. This produces a very fine grade of leather for riding bridles, russet reins, etc.

TO COLOR EDGES OF SADDLE FLAPS.

Use a strong solution of soda, apply it to the freshly cut edges, and, when nearly dry, rub with a woolen rag until a good polish is produced.

HARNESS OIL.

An excellent oil for team and farm harness is made of beef tallow and neat's-foot oil, as follows : Melt 3 pounds of pure tallow, but do not heat it up to a boil ; then pour in gradually 1 pound of neat's-foot oil, and stir until the mass is cold ; if properly stirred, the two articles will become thoroughly amalgamated, and the grease will be smooth and soft ; if not well stirred, the tallow will granulate and show fine white specks when cold. The addition of a little bone black will improve this oil for general use.

NEW-YORK, March 30th, 1876.

. . . Our customers who buy it once buy again, which is a very good sign that it gives satisfaction.

. . . It is without doubt the most desirable, cheapest and neatest Harness mounting that can be used for fine harness.

R. S. LUQUEER & CO.

Wholesale dealers in Foreign and Domestic Saddlery Hardware.

PHILADELPHIA, April 10th, 1876.

. . . The Mountings have invariably given satisfaction. I consider them the most beautiful and durable Mountings in the market for use in fine harness. . . .

SAMUEL R. PHILLIPS.

Manufacturer of fine Carriage and Road Harness.

PHILADELPHIA, Pa., April 13th, 1876.

. . . . We now use on all our work, exclusively, rubber buckles and rings, very rarely using the leather covered, unless specially ordered. This we do, not only because they give much more satisfaction, but help sustain our reputation for long wearing work, etc. They look equally neat and tasteful as the leather covered when first put on the work, and in after years very much neater, and to the consumer, are considerably less expensive to use, in the long run, than the covered. We speak conscientiously from practical experience and careful watching, and we hesitate in no instance to recommend them in the strongest terms to all our customers, who have, in many instances, thanked us, afterward, for insisting upon their using them, in place of leather covered. We cheerfully recommend them to all makers of the highest class of work. . . . .

HENRY G. HÆDRICH & SONS.

Wholesale Manufacturers of Harness and Saddlery.

NEWARK, N. J., March 27th, 1876.

. . . . . . They are the neatest in style and finish of any known to the trade, are the most durable and are most sought after by those who use *fine* Harness.

Very respectfully,

PETERS & CALHOUN CO.

Wholesale Manufacturers of Saddles, Harness, etc.

NEWARK, N. J., March 24th, 1876.

. . . . Of the many different kinds of Harness Mountings made and sold that we have used, there are none that have given the satisfaction for either durability or style equal to the Hard Rubber Coated Harness Trimmings made by yourself.

N. J. DEMAREST & CO.

Wholesale Manufacturers of fine Harness.

PHILADELPHIA, March 23d, 1876.

We have sold largely of Hard Rubber Harness Trimmings for several years past, and so far as we know, they have given satisfaction to all our customers. We consider the Rubber Covering a great improvement over Leather for Harness Trimmings.

SCOTT & DAY.

Wholesale Jobbers in Saddlery and Carriage Goods.

BALTIMORE, March 27th, 1876.

. . . In the first place, as dealers, we will say that they have always given great satisfaction to our customers, their only objection being that "*that they lasted to long.*" Then we have had a personal experience with these mountings and can produce a set of single and also a set of double harness made up with these mountings which have been in constant use since the spring of 1870, and the mountings are good yet and give every indication of outlasting the leather. . . . .

H. R. McNALLY & CO.

Importers and Dealers in Saddlery Hardware.

PITTSBURG, March 29th, 1876.

. . . . It has almost entirely superseded all other Trimmings we formerly used, and to our entire satisfaction, and without any complaint from our customers who have worn it, which constitutes one of its strongest points. It suits our atmosphere here, since gold, oroide and other mountings will scarcely ever be bright on account of the amount of coal smoke and sulphur in our air. The entire freedom from rust or tarnish when the mounting becomes old, and its rather increasing than diminishing in its jet black lustre with age is another strong point.

LOUGHREY & FREW.

Harness, Trunks, Blankets, Whips, Robes, etc.

———

St. Louis, March 27th, 1876.

Our customers like *your* goods. *We* like to handle *them.* Those who use them like them, and we consider them reasonable in *price* for the quality.

Yours,　　HAYDENS & ALLEN.

Wholesale Jobbers.

———

Chicago, March 29th, 1876.

Your Rubber Coated Harness Trimmings. . . have given universal satisfaction. They are very hard and wear like iron: retain their color and beauty until worn out.　　SQUIRES BROS. & CO.

Wholesale Dealers in Saddlery Hardware Leather, etc.

———

Rochester, N. Y., March 28th, 1876.

Decidedly the *best trimmings* ever used.

A. V. SMITH & CO.

Manufacturers and Dealers in fine Harness, Carriages, etc.

———

Indianapolis, April 3d, 1876.

. . . . We congratulate you on your accomplishment of what had not heretofore been done, "creating a *new article* of manufacture," which is so full of real merit and of utility.　　AD. HERETH & CO.

Wholesale and Retail Dealers in Harness, Saddles, Bridles, etc.

———

Hamilton, Ont., April 4th, 1876.

. . . . We believe these mountings for beauty and durability are unsurpassed; in fact, are *superior* to any thing yet manufactured.

FIELD & DAVIDSON,

Saddlery Hardware Merchants.

———

Milwaukee, Wis., April 3d, 1876.

. . . I have used your goods in the manufacture of harness and have sold them largely to harness makers, and know of no instance where fault has been found with the quality of them. I consider the goods manufactured under your patent much superior to any coated trimmings I have seen or have knowledge of.

GEO. DYER.

Wholesale Dealer in Saddlery, Milwaukee, Wis.

———

Lexington, Ky , April 19th, 1876.

. . . . We have no hesitancy in saying that we consider it *the best in use.* We have been using the Rubber Mountings some six or eight years, and it has proven eminently satisfactory to us and to our customers.　　THOMPSON & BOYD.

Dealers in Saddles, Harness, etc.

———

St. Louis, April 20th, 1876.

Our experience has enabled us to form an intelligent judgment as to the wearing qualities of the Rubber Coating, and we can sincerely congratulate your company on the great improvement they have offered in Harness Mountings.

HOBLITZELLE & COUSLAND.

Manufacturers and Wholesale Dealers in Saddlery, Harness, etc.

———

Chicago, March, 1876.

For neatness and durability they are unsurpassed, and I give them the preference over all other covered or coated Harness Mountings.

B. LANE.

Harness and Horse Furnishing Goods.

INDEX.

————•••————

INDEX.